The
Crystal Ball

How the Dreaming Brain Can See the Future

Louis Ferrante

MAIJ Publishing

ISBN-13: 978-0692439081
ISBN-10: 0692439080

Library of Congress Control Number: 2015907884

MAIJ Publishing
Tampa, Florida

Contents

For Ron and Vicki Weiner
and
Danny and Soundis Passman

"The distinction between past, present, and future is only a stubbornly persistent illusion."

—Albert Einstein

"The processes of the system [unconscious] are timeless; they are not ordered temporally, are not altered by the passage of time, in fact bear no relation to time at all."

—Sigmund Freud

Author's Note

In my first two books, I wrote about many of my life experiences in the hope that others will benefit from the grave mistakes I've made and the valuable lessons I've learned. The countless fan mails I receive from around the world to that effect have reassured me that my endeavors have not been in vain and have offered my conscience a small degree of peace. I wholeheartedly thank everyone who has ever written me, believing, as Einstein has said, that "the life of the individual has meaning only insofar as it aids in making the life of every living thing nobler and more beautiful."

In *The Three Pound Crystal Ball*, I again relate my experiences though they are of a very different nature than the experiences included in my previous books. I do so in the belief that they may shed light on one of the many mysteries which lies behind the seemingly impenetrable curtain of our existence.

Preface
Prisoners of Time

Convicts often use the phrase "doing time." The entire prison experience is a constant reminder of the phenomenon of Time. Through prison sentences, the justice system uses Time to punish convicts, and their movements inside a prison are strictly coordinated by clocks and bells that chime on the hour. So cons spend a lot of time thinking about Time. But cons aren't alone in their obsession with Time.

Since the beginning of recorded history the concept of Time has intrigued us all. And how we've dealt with it reveals much about our universal character. We have a penchant for organization so we created the calendar, holding Time to a schedule. We're inventive but also controlling so we invented devices to control Time's movements, beginning with the sundial. But just like the dial's shadow, Time vanishes. Next, we came up with the sand glass; let's isolate Time like a genie in a bottle. But just like sand, Time slips through our hands. We tend to destroy what we cannot control so we tried to drown Time in the water clock. But Time continued to flow like a river, dragging us along. In the course of all this, we sliced and diced Time into seconds, minutes, and hours—divide and conquer, our favorite tactic. Yet Time still conquered us. In the age of discovery, we searched for the fountain of youth in an attempt to frustrate Time's merciless resolve to age us like grapes on a vine. No luck, couldn't find it.

What to do? We invented the pocket watch so we could hold Time in the palm of our hands and tuck it away in our pockets; out of sight, out of mind. Yet Time still ticked, methodically beating against our chests, a counter movement to our every heartbeat which is a constant reminder of our internal clocks that also tick away the moments of our lives.

At last we surrendered and accepted that we're prisoners of Time; we strapped Time to our wrists like a handcuff and called it a wristwatch. Here it remains until each of us has served out our life sentence on earth. But around the same time that we accepted this lifelong handcuff, Albert Einstein came along and gave us his special theory of relativity which infers that "Time is an illusion." With that, we were back in the fight.

Beyond proving that Time is an illusion, Einstein also pointed out that Time cannot exist without Space. No Space, no Time. The idea of Space being inextricably intertwined with Time predates Einstein. A number of other writers including Arthur Schopenhauer—whom Einstein read and admired—believed that Space and Time were inseparable. But we couldn't, shall we say, catch the two of them in bed together until Einstein published his theory of relativity which confirmed the idea of SpaceTime.[1]

A brilliant mathematician named Hermann Minkowski, who happened to be one of Einstein's teachers (and referred to Einstein, while he was his student, as a "lazy dog"), worked out the mathematics of SpaceTime and is quoted as saying, "From now onwards space by itself and time by itself will recede completely to become mere shadows and only a type of union of the two will stand independently on its own."

Having established this peculiar bond between Space and Time, let us apply the principle of SpaceTime to the human mind and ponder the question: Does Time exist in the mind? First, let us ask ourselves if the mind and brain are one and the same. Members of both the philosophical and scientific

---

[1] In *On the Fourfold Root of the Principle of Sufficient Reason,* Schopenhauer wrote, "The representation of coexistence is impossible in Time alone; it depends, for its completion, upon the representation of Space; because in mere Time, all things follow one another, and in mere Space all things are side by side, it is accordingly only by the *combination of Time and Space* that the representation of coexistence arises."

communities have argued over this question for centuries but let's shelve the deeper questions for the moment and just look at mental and physical attributes. To emphasize the difference between mind and brain, imagine you go to the doctor and tell him you have a splitting headache that just won't go away. He leans back in his seat and asks you, "How was your childhood?" Or you visit a doctor and tell him you're contemplating suicide and he says, "Take two aspirin and call me in the morning."

The brain is a physical organ that grows; it can swell, be photographed, and operated on with surgical instruments. It can even be placed in a jar and observed by a mad scientist or pickled and eaten by Hannibal Lecter along with some fava beans and Chianti. In contrast, the mind cannot be heard, seen, smelled, felt, or touched—jarred or eaten.

A thought does not exist in Space, and as Einstein has proven, Time needs Space to exist. Therefore, Time cannot exist in a spaceless mind. Maybe that's why, though the future is securely hidden from us, now and then the little man in charge of security draws back the curtain and allows us a glimpse of moments that have not yet ticked away. The intent of this book is to grab hold of that curtain and yank it open. In doing so, we'll draw on the genius of Albert Einstein, noted above, and Sigmund Freud who I'll speak of presently.

Until Sigmund Freud came along, dreams had always been thought of as portents of the future. This belief spanned the ancient world from Mesopotamia to Greece and Rome. Anyone who has read the Bible would know that dreams play a large part in guiding the destiny of the Hebrews, and in turn, humankind. In the Bible's book of Genesis, Joseph explained Pharaoh's dream of fat cows eating thin cows to mean that a drought would soon deplete Egypt of its food supply and therefore he had better start making plans for the future. Pharaoh believed Joseph's interpretation, heeded his advice, and Egypt was saved. Abraham and Jacob also had dreams that told them what the future held, all of which came to fruition.

These biblical stories, true or not, form but a single stone on a mountain of evidence that proves the Ancients, whether wrong or right, believed that dreams could reveal the future.

Let's leave the ancient world and return to Sigmund Freud who was born in the wake of a scientific revolution that sought to undermine all forms of superstition. Freud almost singlehandedly did away with the notion that dreams could foretell the future when he published his seminal work, *The Interpretation of Dreams.* At first, book sales were slow and it took years to sell out the initial printing of six hundred copies. But eventually the book took off and its success offered a brand new take on dreams that categorically dismissed outdated biblical stories and showed that the prophetic (or precognitive) dreams contained in them demanded as much skepticism as blood-red rivers and parting seas.

In this book, we will get around to the motive behind Freud's denial of precognitive dreams but first let's ask ourselves: Has science successfully disproved precognitive dreams? Quite the contrary. In fact, there have been plenty of scientific discoveries hatched in the sleeping brain that have benefitted the world.

In the nineteenth century, Professor Dmitri Mendeleyev said, "I saw in a dream a table where all the elements fell into place as required. Awakening, I immediately wrote it down on a piece of paper." That table Mendeleyev saw in his dream is now known as the Periodic Table of the Elements. And anyone who has sat in a high school chemistry classroom can now imagine this overwhelming chart floating through Mendeleyev's dreaming mind.

How about the discovery of insulin? My nephew is a juvenile diabetic so this one hits home. In the twentieth century, Frederick Banting—who was knighted for this—woke up one night from a dream, the content of which led to the discovery of insulin. My nephew's life is saved twice a day, along with millions of other diabetics, the direct result of a dream.

Otto Loewi won a Nobel Prize in 1936 for work that eventually contributed to unraveling the now known "on-off switch" that regulates our sleep-wake cycles. And one of Loewi's greatest discoveries came to him, rather appropriately, in a dream. In Loewi's words: "I awoke, turned on the light, and jotted down a few notes on a tiny slip of thin paper. Then I fell asleep again. It occurred to me at six o'clock in the morning that during the night I had written down something most important."

Dreams have also led to some of the world's most well-known musical creations. Robert Schumann, George Frideric Handel, and Richard Wagner are just three composers who recorded songs they had heard in their dreams. Wagner could hardly believe it himself when *Tristan and Isolde* popped out of his dreaming mind. "My poor brain could never have invented such a thing." Nor could Paul McCartney believe it when the hit song, *Yesterday,* popped out of his dreaming mind. "I woke up with a lovely tune in my head…I got out of bed, sat at the piano…I liked the melody a lot but because I'd dreamed it, I couldn't believe I'd written it."

What about the novel? The plot for Robert Louis Stevenson's *Dr. Jekyll and Mr. Hyde* sprung directly from a dream; one man with two minds, how apropos. Franz Kafka and Jack Kerouac have also written novels that stemmed from a dream, as did Mary Shelley. Shelley, the author of *Frankenstein*, first saw the monster in a dream and thought, upon awakening, "What terrified me will terrify others, and I need only describe the specter which had haunted my midnight pillow." D. H. Lawrence once commented, "I can never decide whether my dreams are the result of my thoughts, or my thoughts are the result of my dreams." I personally think it's both; as Minkowski has said of SpaceTime, "A type of union of the two will stand independently on its own."

Can creative thoughts that lead to inventions, musical compositions, and literary works actually spring from a place in the mind where Time does not exist in terms of past, present, and future? During an interview, Einstein once said, "There comes a point where the mind takes a higher plane of knowledge, but can never prove how it got there. All great discoveries have involved such a leap."

According to Einstein, we can deduce that new inventions have already been invented since "Time is an illusion." Is it possible that the inventor need only catch up with his or her own invention? Since the inventor can only recall the past but is unaware of the future until it becomes the present, the inventor may believe that what he or she has invented is new, which of course it is, but only in the moment we're trapped in. Einstein wouldn't even accept applause for his own brilliant discoveries. "I claim credit for nothing," he said in October of 1929. "Everything is determined, the beginning as well as the end." Take a moment to think about this. And remember, I didn't come up with the basis for any of it, Einstein did when he "dethroned time…a liberation from the unbreakable rule of before and after."

When Crick and Watson discovered the double helix (or poor Rosalind Franklin, but we won't get into that), we suddenly learned that our genetic code is predetermined, all imprinted on that spiral ladder. Wow, who'd have thought? And if our physical existence is predetermined, is it not possible, even likely, that our mental life is also predetermined? This question has been pondered ad nauseam and I sure don't have the answer, but such questions prime us to think outside the box. Remember, Time as we know it does not exist in the mind, or it does exist but in an unfamiliar state, without the boundaries of past, present, and future.

Whenever we broach the subject of seeing into the future, we think of card readers and crystal ballers. And because so many phony psychics are hoodwinking vulnerable people, we tend to disbelieve all of them. But something strange happened to me years before I'd ever imagined becoming an author, long before my books were translated into fifteen languages and I had appeared on television around the world. The incident happened in the early 1990s. I'll state it as it appears in my memoir, which was published in 2008:

We were in the neighbor's living room a few minutes when the front door opened and an attractive older woman walked in and waved. We all said hello, but her eyes fell on me, like she knew me. I didn't recognize her.

She went into the kitchen and called to her husband. He got up and excused himself. When he came out, he looked confused.

"My wife is a psychic," he said to me. "We're married over thirty years. When she feels this strongly about something, she's never wrong. My wife saw a vision when she looked at you. You have a destiny."

Years later, when I began to read, after I learned to write, as I pushed through Manhattan crowds trying to nudge my way into a publisher's office, I remembered that day, and what that woman had said.

I hope this book contributes to that destiny but nonetheless I was a hardened, tattooed thug when that woman had seen me. I had no real thoughts beyond that very day; at best, I could plan as far as the weekend. Yet that woman had glimpsed something strange, far ahead of the moment we were living in. You can believe this or not, heck it's even hard for me to swallow and I was there! But if we're honest with ourselves, most of us have experienced rare glimpses of the future yet only realized it once the event had past; it's called a déjà vu. What is a déjà vu? A fleeting moment. We feel we've been here before. The moment and the feeling are gone, just like that. So fast yet so real. When it happens, we might elbow the person next to us and say, "Wow, I just had a déjà vu." But how can we prove it when the feeling passes so quickly and cannot be retrieved? Searching for proof of a déjà vu is like trying to put the smoke from a smoking gun into an evidence bag; can't do it, it's gone.

But a good detective doesn't quit. In this book, I plan to gather evidence and prove that Time has been guilty of committing fraud. To achieve this, I'll play the role of prosecutor and treat my evidence as that which is normally presented in a court case. I'll begin with my own observational evidence and will, at times, call on Albert Einstein as a witness for the prosecution. I'll also subpoena Sigmund Freud who may at first appear as a hostile witness but I intend to break him down on cross examination and draw him over to my side. You, dear reader, have been called for jury duty. I ask that you carefully weigh the evidence with an open mind before reaching a final verdict.

Allow me to present my case.

Introduction
A Shark in the Dark

I had never read a book in my life until I was locked away in a prison cell. About a year into my sentence, I read my first book and fell in love with reading. I was six years into my thirteen year sentence when I began representing myself and reversed my federal conviction. I would have been released almost immediately if not for a state sentence I still had to serve. While waiting to be transferred from federal prison to state prison, I appealed my state sentence (not the actual conviction) and had excellent legal grounds for a resentencing that would qualify me for an immediate release. While I awaited a response from the New York State Appellate Court, the possibilities were clear. At best, I'd win the state appeal, get resentenced to time served and be home free. At worst, I'd lose the appeal and serve another two years in state custody before my mandatory release date.

By this time, I had been reading eighteen hours a day, every single day, for several years. I knew how much books had improved my mind and it's likely, had I never gone to prison, I'd have never picked up a book. Although I desperately wanted my freedom, I also knew deep down that I would never again have as much time to read as I did in prison. Because of this, as crazy as it might sound, a part of me wanted to stay. But another part of me knew that even a slight desire to stay in that hell was insane.

These confusing thoughts were running through my head when I went to sleep one night and awoke after the following dream:

I was alone in a stone cell situated at the top of a tower, something like the Tower of London. Piles of books were scattered around my cell.

Holding a book in my hands, I stared out of a barred window down at a moat below.

At regular intervals, a shark fin sliced through the water in the moat, circling the larger fortress that housed me. I could see through the clear, shallow water that the shark fin was not real but mechanical, pulled through the water by a sturdy chain, like the chains that pull cars through a car wash.

As I watched the shark fin below, a prison guard knocked on my cell door, opened it, and said, "Ferrante, you're free to go." I turned around, held up my book, and said, "I'll pass, I'm reading."

The guard left, slamming my cell door behind him, and I awoke.

Immediately upon awakening, I interpreted the meaning of the dream as such: Prison life allowed me the luxury of reading all day and night without the ordinary worries of daily survival, all of which were provided for me by the institution; the free world is much too demanding to allow for such leisure. The dream appeared to be a simple reflection of the inner dilemma I was experiencing before I had gone to sleep.

Apparently, this spare-time-to-read conflict running through my conscious thoughts was now haunting my dreams. I questioned my sanity, wondering if I was afflicted by a deeper anxiety. Was I using books as a convenient excuse to stay in prison when in fact I had become institutionalized, fearing, as many convicts do, the responsibility of freedom?[2]

---

[2] This is a common phenomenon in prison and one that directly relates to the high rate of recidivism. I've seen one man stab another to avoid being released from prison. On another occasion, I walked a hardened con to the prison gates on the day of his release where he literally cried on my shoulder, terrified of what awaited him in the free world. Several months later, he was back in jail. Erich Fromm dissected this curious mindset in his book, *Escape from Freedom,* as did Eric Hoffer in his masterpiece, *The True Believer.* But no environment offers a better display of the idea in action as

This was the scary thought this dream left me to ponder. The true meaning of the dream was yet to unravel.

Months later, the New York State Appellate Court denied my appeal. I was promptly shackled and sent from the holdover jail to a prison in the Adirondack Mountains of northern New York. Here I would serve the remainder of my sentence in a prison that was originally built in 1903 as the very first New York state-operated tuberculosis sanatorium[3]. After settling into this prison, which always involves standing up to bullies who test every newcomer, I got right back into my rhythm of reading eighteen hours a day.

Once again, I was in the hell of prison—but literary heaven. And the hell part was easier to bear, the reason being was that fate had spoken to me in a strange way. Here's how it happened:

Shortly after I had arrived in this prison, I was sent to a third floor tier block which was the highest floor in the building. I was assigned to a cell with a view of the Adirondack Mountains. I spent my days reading, and books quickly piled up around me, cluttering my cell.

One afternoon, as I sat reading beside my barred window, lunch was called. After the prison guard hollered, "On the chow," my fellow convicts emptied the tier block and raced to the chow hall. I was immersed in a good book and decided to skip chow; later on, I would eat something from my locker where I kept some snacks.

Now and then, the guard on duty will call chow then walk the tier block to see if anyone has stayed behind, and inquire as to why (for example, a convict may stay behind intending to rob another convict's cell). On this particular

---

does prison.

[3] Until I wrote this book, I did not know that the prison I was housed in was only four miles away from Einstein's summer cottage on Lower Saranac Lake. Here, Einstein received news that the atomic bomb had been dropped on Hiroshima, to which he replied, "Oh, my God."

occasion, the guard noticed me, poked his head into my cell, and said, "Chow time, Ferrante! You going?"

I turned around to face the guard and raised the book in my hand. "I'll pass, I'm reading."

After the guard walked away, I turned back toward the window. Below that window, beyond the high fences and coils of razor wire, was a single-lane paved road on which a security truck regularly circled the perimeter of the prison. The truck is driven by a prison guard assigned to perimeter duty. And at the very moment I had turned around in my chair, the security truck was passing on the road below. Suddenly it all clicked. This old prison was the stone fortress in that shark dream I had dreamt months before. The single-lane paved road was the moat that encircled the fortress. And the security truck was the mechanical shark fin that circled the moat. My third floor cell, the highest in the building, was the stone cell in the tower. The guard, myself, and the piles of books around me were exactly the same as in my dream. The guard's question was also similar, and my response, "I'll pass, I'm reading," in both my dream and in reality, was attributed to my desire to continue reading without interruption.

I couldn't help but smile, finding comfort in the thought that my extra time in prison was, aside from well-deserved punishment, my destiny. My education was not yet complete. And my already passionate pursuit of knowledge now became maniacal.

Intrigued by the clear and undeniable meaning of my shark dream, I sought to understand more about the dreaming brain. For reasons I'll explain later, I began my research with Sigmund Freud's *The Interpretation of Dreams*. In this book, Freud commented about one dream in particular that was strikingly familiar to variations of a dream I had had since my youth. Freud refers to the dream of a man named Maury, and my own conclusion, based on personal experiences, greatly differs from Freud's interpretation. Maury's dream and my similar dreams will be discussed in subsequent chapters.

Over the next two years, I recorded my dreams while also searching for neurological evidence to support my experiential interpretation of Maury's dream. Though prison is a loud, chaotic place, it's also a very lonely place but the loneliness would contribute to my focus, concentration, and recollection of relevant dreams.

In 2003, I was released from prison and re-entered the free world after being confined to a cell for nearly a decade. In that time, I had given myself the education I so desperately needed and had taught myself the art of writing by reading the masters of classic literature and carefully studying their writing styles. I was determined to become a professional writer but found the literary world to be as tough as prison. My background may have contributed to the cold reception I received everywhere I went but I was determined to break in.

After struggling to merely survive for several years while also pursuing what was starting to feel like a pipe dream, I finally met Bill Yosses who was the White House pastry chef for both the Bush and Obama administrations. Bill introduced me to a literary agent who was willing to take me on; it was the break I needed. Not that my quest became much easier but it was a big step in the right direction. I would go on to publish two books in fifteen languages, and write, produce, and host my own television series that aired around the globe. But from the day I had stepped out of prison I was compelled to file away my earlier notes on dreams knowing that, once the world took me seriously, I could revisit them. This I would do after an uncanny sequence of events called to mind the many thoughts I'd written about the dreaming mind and nudged me to publish the book you are now reading.

It was 2013 and I was packing for a business trip to London. At the time, I was in the midst of reading a thick biography on Albert Einstein but preferred a more portable book for the airplane ride. Already in the mood for science, I grabbed a thin paperback biography of Isaac Newton and threw it in my backpack.

For the flight, I wore a wristwatch with a black band and packed another with a brown band. I caught a red-eye out of JFK and landed at Heathrow the next morning with the day to myself. Whenever I travel for business, jet lag usually stops me from seeing the sights upon my arrival; I typically go straight to my hotel room and rest up for meetings. But I'd slept well on the plane and felt revived. For some time I had wanted to visit Sigmund Freud's last place of residence, now a museum in London. I checked into my hotel then hailed a cab and headed there.

The tour of Freud's home was awesome; the chair he sat on, the desk he wrote on, and the sofa some confused patient laid on, all right there for visitors to see. After the tour, I grabbed a bite to eat and went back to my hotel room where I showered then sat on my bed with my Newton book. I read for a couple of hours, finished the small book, then dressed for dinner; I was getting together with my colleagues at a local pub. Before leaving the room, I strapped my black watch to my wrist and noticed that the watch had stopped; I assumed the battery had died. I took the watch off and exchanged it for the brown watch. After bringing that watch up to London time, I strapped it to my wrist and about ten minutes later, I realized that it had also stopped ticking. Both watches had told the accurate time at home which meant they'd stopped, at most, within several hours of each other. This was odd since the watches were not purchased together nor did I have the batteries replaced at the same time.

There were no ghosts or goblins floating around the room or a fuzzy TV screen calling for Carol Ann, but this curious coincidence brought Time to the forefront of my mind. I sat on the bed to think, holding a wristwatch in each hand. On the hotel night table was a book that had a sketch of Isaac Newton's face on the cover. On my night table at home was a book with a photograph of Albert Einstein's face on the cover. And for the better part of that day, there was an image of Sigmund Freud's face in my mind. Were these titans speaking to me from their graves? Of course not, though it would be cool to think so. I did, however, draw an immediate connection between Time, science, and dreams, and I was inspired, at that very moment, to revisit the notes I had written in my dark, dank prison cell more than ten years earlier. I was established now, maybe I'd be taken seriously.

Upon my arrival home from London, I pulled out my box of notes on Time and dreams and began to sift through it. The many loose papers in that box were puzzle pieces I needed to organize in order to construct my theory of the dreaming brain. But before I relate to you the content of those notes and speculate as to the potential impact they might have on our understanding of Time, I'll first rewind to a much earlier period in my life when, unbeknownst to me, the seeds of my theory had been sown.

Chapter One
A *Head*-On Collision

     The first year of my life was spent with my parents and my older sister in a one-car garage that had been converted into a small basement apartment. After a year of living here, we moved to a two-story home on the same avenue, just a few blocks away. My parent's bedroom was on the second floor, located at the back of the house; their room overlooked the Long Island Expressway. My sister and I shared a bedroom at the front of the house, also on the second floor; our room overlooked the campus of Queens College. (Unfortunately, the proximity did not move me to attend.) On the street corner below our bedroom window was a stop sign that halted traffic flowing from the side street onto the avenue, which ran parallel to the college campus.

     For any number of reasons, student drivers sometimes blew the stop sign: a rush to get to class or more cars than parking spaces which caused people to race around for an empty spot. Sometimes drivers inched up to see beyond the parked cars that blocked the crosswalk and were blasted by other cars in the process; other times they simply may not have seen the stop sign. Whatever the reason, at least once or twice a year, I'd hear a loud crash outside my house, the result of a car accident on the corner.

     I don't know if I was ten, eleven, or twelve, but around that age I vividly recall a curious type of dream that sometimes preceded the collisions on the corner. For the most part, these dreams were no different from other dreams myself or anyone else might have, combining material from our memories into nonsensical scenes we don't always understand. But there was one major difference between these particular dreams and others I had had: prior to the accidents on my corner, my dream would unravel in such a way that the dream's climax produced a loud noise—inside my dreaming head—that perfectly coincided with the actual noise caused by the collision outside. For example, in one of my dreams, my sister and I were arguing over who would throw out the trash. The argument began at the dinner table but somehow moved upstairs to our bedroom where, oddly enough, my sister had dragged the trash pail. After arguing a bit longer, I at last accepted that it was my turn to throw out the trash. The outdoor garbage pails were kept in the driveway below our bedroom window so I opened the window and dropped the pail straight down.

I watched the pail fall two stories before it hit the pavement with a loud crash. I awoke, heard a commotion outside, and quickly realized that the noise in my dream was not caused by the trash pail hitting the pavement, but two cars colliding on the corner. Thus, while my sister and I were carrying on an argument within the confines of my brain, two people in the real world were driving along two different routes, and heading straight for a collision. Neither the drivers nor I was aware of this prior to its occurrence but somewhere in the folds of my brain, actors had been cast, dialogue had been scripted and spoken, and a plot was carefully chosen and precisely timed so that the dream's finale—the loud crash of the pail—perfectly corresponded with the actual noise of the automobile collision outside my window. Upon awakening, it became obvious to me, even as a boy, that the dreaming brain was well aware of the impending calamity. I can vividly remember shaking my head, amazed. When I tried to explain these dreams to my parents they'd just smile and go about their business.

Although I had experienced countless variations of this same dream throughout my youth, I only began to wonder what questions they raise, or answers they provide, with regard to Time, while thrust into the abyss of solitude where Time was my enemy and books were my only friends.

Let us enter prison.

Chapter Two
The Misinterpretation of Dreams

I had never gone to university and never held a steady job in my life. I began stealing in my early teens and became a career criminal after finishing high school. This career lasted until the age of twenty-five when I was hauled off to prison. I was indicted by the FBI, the U.S. Secret Service, and the Nassau County Organized Crime Task Force. In the end, after hiring and firing seven different attorneys, and eventually representing myself, I was fortunate to avoid a life sentence.

While in prison, I decided to change my life. I educated myself for years but more importantly, I accepted responsibility for my crimes and I began to think about the roots of my criminal behavior. Where did I go wrong? And why? I felt the need to address such questions in order to move forward with my life. Once I had honestly answered these questions, I sought to help other prisoners understand the origins of their own criminal behavior and persuaded some to accept responsibility for the actions that led them to prison. In just about every case, there was a host of contributing factors beyond each man's control, but I convinced most convicts that the final decisions that led them to prison were their own. Oftentimes, my cell became the equivalent of an unlicensed psychiatrist's office. I'd ask questions about a convict's early youth, resembling, I might imagine, a dumbed-down version of Sigmund Freud. But my "patients" weren't that bright either so the playing field was level and I was able to help quite a few men.

So, rather oddly, I had somewhat mimicked Freud's style of psychoanalytic inquiry before I had read any of his books. Then one day I came across one of Freud's works in the prison library titled, *Civilization and Its Discontents.* The book was old and musty smelling but the content was absolutely brilliant, so much so that I read it a second time. Given Freud's genius, apparent in the book mentioned above, I therefore chose his work, *The Interpretation of Dreams,* as an introduction into the subject matter after realizing the clear meaning of my shark dream. As noted earlier in my introduction, many of Freud's dream interpretations were insightful while others, I felt, were bizarre. And then there is that dream dreamt by a man named Maury which called to mind my stop sign dreams. Freud relates Maury's dream as follows:

"A dream dreamt by Maury has become famous. He was ill and lying in his room in bed, with his mother sitting beside him, and dreamt that it was during the Reign of Terror. After witnessing a number of frightful scenes of murder, he was finally himself brought before the revolutionary tribunal. There he saw Robespierre, Marat, Fouquier-Tinville and the rest of the grim heroes of those terrible days. He was questioned by them, and after a number of incidents which were not retained in his memory, was condemned, and led to the place of execution surrounded by an immense mob. He climbed on to the scaffold and was bound to the plank by the executioner. It was tipped up. The blade of the guillotine fell. He felt his head being separated from his body, woke up in extreme anxiety—and found that the top of the bed had fallen down and had struck his cervical vertebrae just in the way in which the blade of the guillotine would actually have struck them."

Take note of how long the above scenes would take to play out in sequence even if the mind were able to dispense with the scenes in rapid succession. At least on the face of this, it appears that Maury's dreaming brain is recognizing an event—his bed falling down—before it actually occurs, and therefore prepares a dream scenario capable of mimicry. As you can see, Maury's dream is very similar to the stop sign dreams I had dreamt in my youth. Freud goes on to say:

"This dream was the basis of an interesting discussion between Le Lorrain (1894) and Egger (1895) in the *Revue philosophique.* The question raised was whether and how it was possible for a dreamer to compress such an apparently superabundant quantity of material into the short period elapsing between his perceiving the rousing stimulus and his waking."

Here, Freud does not speculate as to the possibility of the dreaming brain's capacity to recognize an event before it actually happens. Instead, he relates a discussion between Le Lorrain and Egger that questions if Maury's dreaming mind can stuff an entire sequence of events from the French Revolution, interrogations and all, into the infinitesimally small durational period between the crash of the bed and his waking.

If Maury's mind, or the rest of our minds for that matter, are able to "compress an apparently superabundant quantity of material" into such a "short period" then the dreaming mind is not subject to the same properties of Time that govern our waking minds. And if the mind is not subject to the properties of Time as we imagine them to be while awake, and past, present, and future are all the same, as Einstein has pointed out, then why can't the mind, which can arguably stuff a number of scenes from the French Revolution into a nano-second, just as easily recognize an event in the future before it happens? Once the mind has dispensed with our traditional understanding of its laws, as Freud is indeed willing to consider but in a different light, this unlawfulness cannot be subject to a penal code; it's all or nothing. And if it's all, then my hunch that the mind is recognizing an external event before it occurs is just as strong as Freud's conjecture.[4]

---

[4] Einstein has described SpaceTime as deformable and the compression of Time is a well-known consequence of relativity. So it is possible that Time is highly compressed in the dream state. Thus, Freud may be correct. And such would only reinforce my conviction that the mind is glimpsing the future. How and why is the basis of this book.

An additional problem I have with this "compress" idea is that, if the dream narrative were compressed into a nano-second, it would be difficult, probably impossible, to recall in such vivid detail.

For example, imagine standing on a street corner and carrying on a conversation with someone when suddenly a multi-vehicle accident occurs at the intersection. If asked what took place you wouldn't be able to provide many details before a sight or sound drew your attention to the accident or impending accident. At best, your recollection would be fragmentary; under such circumstances, eyewitness accounts almost always prove to be highly inaccurate or lacking in meaningful detail. Now, if we were to play the accident back on video captured from cameras posted above the traffic lights, maybe even in slow motion, we'd be able to see and describe all the little details occurring at the intersection prior to the accident. By the same token, I do not believe that a warp speed dream compressed into a nano-second can be recollected in such vivid detail.

With regard to Maury's dream, Freud finally commits himself to Le Lorrain and Egger's viewpoint:

"Dreams such as the one dreamt by Maury of his own guillotining seem to show that a dream is able to compress into a very short space of time an amount of perceptual matter far greater than the amount of ideational matter that can be dealt with by our waking mind."

Since this is possible, let's backtrack from the argument I have just made above and imagine that this compression idea is valid since there may be a nano-second between "the rousing stimulus and [Maury's] waking." The first question I would ask is how much "perceptual matter" can the mind compress into an actual nano-second? If the mind is not bound by the laws of Time and can relive a number of scenes from "the Reign of Terror" in the space of a nano-second, is there no limit to what events it can squeeze into that nano-second? Can I recite Gibbon's *The History of the Decline and Fall of the Roman Empire*? Can I listen to Beethoven's complete symphonies? Possibly. But even if I can come around to accepting this notion I'm nevertheless left to question our inability to place a precise measurement on how much perceptual matter the mind can compress into that nano-second.

Still, let's try and imagine that the mind can indeed compress a sequence of events into a nano-second, or, as in Maury's dream, a morbid drama from the French Revolution. The dreaming mind would be exhibiting a peculiar dispensation of Time's properties, an unlawfulness that, once established, should be able to perform in another direction: the ability to glimpse an event in Time before it actually arrives in the present moment. For me, I can just as easily imagine that Maury's dreaming mind, unlawful of Time as we've just established, has spied the future and prepared a dream to meet its arrival. Remember, Einstein has taught us that Time is an illusion and that Time needs Space to exist. The mind is spaceless and therefore timeless. Thus, past, present, and future, on some subconscious level, may all be the same.

Lastly, what of my stop sign dreams, which are very similar in nature to Maury's dream? There is no nano-second to work with. According to Freud, Le Lorrain, and Egger's hypothesis, my dreaming mind would only be aware of the crash *when* the crash actually occurs, not even a nano-second beforehand. In fact, my mind would only know about the crash when it hears the sound caused by the crash which is a nano-second *after* the crash, given the fact that the noise from the collision must travel from the metal car bumpers to my ears which is at least a hundred feet away in distance.[5] In such a

---

[5] When I was a boy, the campus of Queens College had a baseball field that I could see from my front porch. Whenever a batter swung, I was amazed that I could see the bat hit the ball a moment or two before I'd hear the sound. In addition to this external time lag caused by sound travel, as exemplified by my example above, there is also an internal time lag, first

case, my mind, which is receiving "the rousing stimulus" *after* the crash, would have to conjure up a quick story, then rewind that story or somehow make me believe it is occurring prior to the interruption, and compress that same story into that earlier moment *which in fact follows the interruption* in order to trick me into believing the dream came first, and the dream's climax—which also *followed* the external noise—perfectly corresponds with the external noise. This scenario is ridiculous on the face of it. However, if one were to argue that it can still happen since the mind is not bound by the laws of Time, then we're also free to ponder what I see as an even greater probability: Could Maury's dream have been spurned by an internal brain mechanism that was given advance notice that his bed was about to collapse? The brain, having glimpsed the future, albeit the very near future, thereby spins a dream, the climax of which perfectly coincides with the collapse.

Let's act the part of a good detective. To do so, we'll treat this conundrum as a crime. A good detective will try to discover what motive lies behind a crime. Our first question should be why the dreaming brain would operate in this manner; what is the motive? Isaac Newton taught us that the universe is governed by certain laws. I believe the human brain, our three pound universe, also functions in accordance with certain laws. I therefore knew there must be a motive.

---

discovered in the late 1970s by Benjamin Libet. The results that stemmed from Libet's experiments proved that our sensory detectors take time to transmit signals to our central nervous systems, and from there, relay them to our brains. So even though we feel we're experiencing the events around us in real time, there is an approximate 80 milli-second time lag. Luckily we're not programmed to recognize this delay so the immediate past feels like the present.

Libet also observed that our brains fire before we even make a decision to act. Libet said, "The brain decides to initiate or at least prepare to initiate the act before there is any reportable subjective awareness that such a decision has taken place." This leaves us to wonder how much free will we really have. Maybe Rene Descartes was wrong; "*It* thinks, therefore I am," may be more accurate.

Before moving on, let's take a brief look at this special man named Maury since his dream, and more importantly, his exhausting work, plays a central role in our investigation.

Chapter Three
Who Was Maury?

Louis Ferdinand Alfred Maury was a French physician and archivist who was interested in the study of sleep and dreams. As a means to research dreams, Maury set up a nineteenth century sleep lab, designed to establish the effects of external stimuli on the dreaming mind. Maury's favorite subject was himself, and he wasn't the first person to experiment on himself in the name of science.

There have been a number of other men and women who have experimented on themselves, like Sir Humphry Davy, whose early death was most likely attributed to testing toxic chemicals on himself. Jonas Salk, famous for discovering the polio vaccine, first tested the vaccine on himself. Even Sigmund Freud got in on the self-experiments, coking it up and giving the stuff away like Disco Johnny when he imagined cocaine could help the world of medicine.[6]

An old saying in the court of law states, "He who represents himself has a fool for an attorney." Applying this adage to science, I'll slightly modify it and say, "He who experiments on himself has a

---

[6] Freud began to research cocaine in April of 1884, long before he became famous for psychoanalysis. He observed cocaine's influence on himself and others whom he supplied with the drug while hoping to apply it in some innovative way that would bring him world acclaim. A colleague of his, Carl Koller, beat him to the punch when Koller discovered that cocaine could anesthetize the eye during eye surgery.

genius for a researcher but a fool for a subject." This adage applies, of course, when the subject exposes him or herself to life-threatening dangers. In the case of Maury and his dream research, however, there was no real danger besides loss of sleep which I'm sure he made up for the following day, keeping his mind fresh for more loss of sleep.

Maury reportedly studied "more than 3000 recollections of dreams" in which he had "accomplices awaken him at specific times and after presenting specific sensory stimuli." For example, when water was dropped on Maury's forehead, he dreamt he was sweating like a pig while guzzling white wine in Italy. When a hot iron was brought close to his face, robbers were burning his feet with hot coals. Maury correctly concluded that external sensory stimuli can trigger a chain of associations in the dreaming mind where memory is used to spin a dream and incorporate the external stimuli into that dream.

Maury is credited as the first dream researcher who was able to record numerous examples of a process by which the dreaming mind seamlessly incorporates external sensory stimuli into a dream; this process is known as Dream Incorporation.[7]

---

[7] The seeds of Dream Incorporation were planted by a Scottish physician named Robert MacNish (1802-1837) who was the first to observe and record incorporation dreams. Sadly, MacNish died young and in contrast to Maury, receives little credit for his groundbreaking work.

Now that we've established the genesis of Dream Incorporation, let's explore duration with regard to Maury's guillotine dream.

To do so, it's necessary to introduce three brainiacs who were drawn together at the University of Chicago in the 1950s: Eugene Aserinsky, Nathaniel Kleitman, and William Dement. Aserinsky and Dement were students at the time and Kleitman was their dissertation advisor. In a flash of genius, not unlike Einstein's idea of relativity, Aserinsky discovered REM sleep. He was studying the flickering eyelids of sleeping subjects when it occurred to him that their rapid eye movement (REM) was directly related to dreaming. This may sound obvious to some, but so did the wheel—after the first caveman rolled one past his drinking buddies and someone said, "I could've thought of that," then burped and took another swig of beer.

Aserinksy bounced his idea off of his mentor, Kleitman, and the two men are credited with the discovery of REM sleep. Dement, who figures into our story, is the third brainiac in this triumvirate, who went on to become a leading authority on dreams and also founded a modern sleep lab at Stanford University, not unlike Maury's sleep lab. Dement's remarkable dream observations are too long to list and would probably put you to sleep, so I'll only focus on studies that are relevant to the matter at hand.

Dement, using modern equipment that wasn't available to Maury, and focusing on his pal Aserinsky's new discovery of REM sleep, monitored sleepers and recorded what he believed to be the duration of their dreams. He did this by observing the durational period of their rapid eye movements, meaning how long their eyelids flickered.

Next, Dement used what editors and writers are familiar with in the publishing industry: word count. My last two books each had a minimum word count requirement mandated by the publisher. In essence, word count translates into how many pages a book will be, and though not the publisher's concern, it also translates into how many hours it will take the average reader to read the book. In sum, word count is length whether translated into pages, or for our purpose, time.

After an episode of REM sleep, which Dement timed by watching a subject's eyelids, Dement woke up his dreamers and asked them to jot down a description of their dreams. He then compared the number of words each dreamer used to describe a particular dream to the amount of time that dreamer had been immersed in REM sleep. (I'm assuming none of his subjects were like my brother-in-law who can tick off an hour describing a hiccup.) Now remember, in publishing, word count equals the length of a book. By comparing how long a dreamer's eyes were flickering to how many words each dreamer used to describe his or her dreams, Dement confirmed that, during REM sleep, word count also equals the length of a dream. Dement took this one step further in an effort to confirm if a dreamer's guestimate as to the time frame of a particular dream was accurate. Recall that I was sure, even in my youth, that my stop sign dreams had begun some time *before* the collisions occurred outside; Dement did indeed confirm this: Over eighty percent of his sleepers were able to say if the dreams they were experiencing before they were awakened were of a long or short duration, proving what Dement had already concluded from their flickering eyes.

Lastly, unrelated waking experiments contribute to Dement's conclusion noted above. Various tests prove that "willing an act [like, for instance] rotating an object mentally in space, takes exactly the same time as physically manipulating it in one's hand."

I was unaware of these studies when I was collecting my notes and recording my dreams but as you might imagine, when I read about them, they hit me like a breath of fresh air. Still, I wondered why none of the sleep researchers have taken Maury's guillotine dream a step further by questioning if Maury had seen into the future, if only just moments in advance, which duration experiments would prove.

French philosopher and mathematician Rene Descartes' oft-quoted statement, "I think, therefore I am" offers a strong clue to Descartes' approach to science which is super skeptical. Descartes believed, when pursuing a scientific problem, we must doubt and doubt and continue to doubt until we have, if possible, answered every doubt with weighty evidence. In honor of Descartes, this scientific process of ultra-critical inquiry is known as Cartesian Skepticism.

Let's apply Cartesian skepticism to the observations I've made of my own stop sign dreams and Maury's guillotine dream. With regard to my stop sign dreams, let's imagine that some of the automobile collisions were preceded by horn blasts or screeching tires. Though I do not recall these sounds being the external stimuli my dreams had to mimic—I only recall the crash—in light of Cartesian skepticism, I'm bound to consider if, on occasion, there was a small time frame between, say a car horn and the collision. Could this small time frame allow my dreaming brain sufficient time to spin a dream, the climax of which would coincide with the external sound of the crash? I don't believe so since we still encounter the problem of duration; even though this small time frame allows my dreaming brain a bit more time to prepare a dream for the oncoming crash, it's still not enough time to include a backstory, for example, the trash pail argument between my sister and I that preceded the crash.

Next, let's consider if an acute auditory sense, or really good hearing, could have heard both cars traveling from different directions, and, recognizing a potential collision, spun a dream just in case the cars collide. In the event the cars pass without incident, my mind simply discards the dream for another, which amounts to one of many forgotten dreams that occur throughout our sleep cycle.

Lastly, though my dreams seem to be specific to the external stimuli, maybe they aren't. If, for instance, the outside collision never occurs, my sister and I somehow resolve the trash pail argument without a bang. No pail hits the pavement and I remain fast asleep. To illustrate this particular possibility, I'll use the making of a documentary film as an example. While hosting a documentary, I may deliver several variations of a concluding thought, allowing the director the freedom to choose

which take he prefers when editing the final cut.
Thus, the conclusion of a story can be altered by
which variation the director chooses. Is it possible
that the dreaming mind is doing the same?

The various alternatives I've just listed
above are highly unlikely but not beyond possibility.
But what of Maury's guillotine dream?

First, there is no possibility of a horn blast or
screeching tires to forewarn Maury of the impending
event. Secondly, Maury's dream is much too
specific to originate without direct intent. The
French Revolution and its use of the guillotine is
probably the absolute best scenario the drama
society of the mind can come up with to disguise a
hard, swift blow to the neck. (If, for example, Maury
was dreaming of a tennis match, and when the bed
collapsed he was suddenly struck in the neck with a
racket, then I can contemplate the possibility that his
dream was open-ended and simply adapted to the
external stimulus when it occurred. But to match the
French Revolution-guillotine scenario so perfectly to
the bed's collapse supports the idea that the
dreaming mind has foreknowledge of the impending
event.)

As for myself, though I don't recall all of the
stop sign dreams from my youth, I do remember
being amazed at how creatively the storyline in my
dream was in sync with the external stimuli.

In 2011, I was invited to speak at The
Economist's Human Potential Summit; a fellow
speaker was Nobel laureate Daniel Kahneman.
Intrigued by Kahneman's ideas, I picked up one of
his books titled, *Thinking Fast and Slow*. In it,
Kahneman writes about "The Moses Illusion" which

explains how events are perceived by the human mind. The Moses Illusion is based on the question: "How many animals did Moses take into the ark?" Very few people spot that Moses is out of place; it was Noah who built the ark and packed it with animals, not Moses.

Noah and Moses are both well-known biblical characters so the inconsistency is subtle and flies past most of us unnoticed. Now try this question: How many people did Manson take into the ark? Replace Noah with Manson and we have a problem; the mind immediately detects a falsehood. And to further show you how the mind works, I never said Charles Manson but most of us in the United States would probably think of him, unless you're a fan of Marilyn Manson. So in order to fool the brain, the association must, as Kahneman writes, "produce cognitive ease" or risk being detected and questioned.

The dreams I am presently discussing, Maury's and my own, must follow the same guidelines as Kahneman has illustrated for us in The Moses Illusion and create cognitive ease or their intent, which is to fool us, cannot succeed.

Having established dream duration and the dreaming brain's capacity for creative storytelling, which involves cognitive ease, allow me to now recap some of the dreams I had recorded in prison.

Pocket Watch of Timeless Dreams. Design by Louis Ferrante, Drawing by Vanessa Montenegro

Chapter Four
Motormouth

In previous chapters I've pointed out that the nano-second between the "rousing stimulus and waking" is far too short a period as to allow the mind to wander off, for example, into various scenes from the French Revolution and recall it all in such vivid detail. And I place particular emphasis on the fact that we cannot accurately measure the sweep of scenarios that can be compressed into this nano-second. Also, as pointed out, William Dement has proven in laboratory studies that the duration of a dream during REM sleep is roughly equal to how long our eyelids have been flickering. But Dement and other experts in the field of dream research have not addressed the major question we're left to ponder from Maury's guillotine dream which proof of duration only emphasizes: Is the dreaming brain aware of the future before it arrives? It's a bold question that needs to be addressed.

For now, let's continue with two more of my own dreams, both of which occurred in prison and offer convincing evidence of the brain's precognitive ability.

The first dream occurred at 12:01 a.m., November 26, 2001. I'll begin with an event from earlier that day that apparently inspired the dreamscape and served as a prelude to the dream. Background for the dream:

Recently, on several occasions, I was by chance in the presence of a fellow convict who, in an effort to sound like an intellect, parrots portions of speech he overhears from television news programs and movies. He uses words out of context and inserts entire sentences, which must have appealed to him, into unrelated conversations.

During the course of the previous day, I had been informed that a particularly quiet inmate was once a high school science teacher. Since I try to glean knowledge from any professionals who find themselves trapped in this hell, I sought him out and found him in the yard. I asked if I could stop by his cell one day so I could ask him some questions about physics. This otherwise quiet man immediately opened up to me, even offering to lend me a helpful book on the subject which he briefly summarized.

The convict I had spoken about earlier was also in the yard and at some point dropped in on our conversation. Unable to pass up an opportunity of injecting some of his own comments, he interrupted us with his lofty, though disconnected, speech. He became increasingly intrigued by the sound of his own voice and seemed to forget he was speaking with two other people. He acted as though he was on a podium at a science convention as he rattled off some lines I imagined he'd heard in a sci-fi movie or had read in a sci-fi novel.

The former science teacher and I, realizing we were witnessing a form of abnormal behavior, patiently allowed him to finish. We then agreed to meet in the future to discuss physics in his cell. (As an aside, I believe this convict's desire to sound intelligent could have been realized had he been born into a different set of circumstances and/or made a different set of decisions. It does not escape me that the teacher and I are also inmates in the same institution, battling with our own mental issues.)

I retired to bed at 11:37 p.m. At 12:01 a.m., I wrestled myself awake to record an interesting dream in which the sole character was the convict who'd interrupted my conversation earlier in the day.

The above recollection was recorded immediately after I recorded the following dream but I have flipped the order of their appearance in light of clarity. And now the dream:

The convict was giving a speech while standing on a podium, most likely the one I had imagined him on earlier that day. True to character, he was attempting to sound like an intellect though the full content of his short speech I do not recall. What I do recall very vividly is that he was speed-talking, rushing through his words and sentences. After only two or three fast sentences without pause, delivered in a huff, the audience began to clap. I awoke and heard the sounds of clapping from another cell along the corridor; a con may have been clapping along to a song or interacting with his cell mate.

There is one major difference that sets this dream apart from similar dreams I've had in the past. The man was talking extremely fast, reminiscent of the old Federal Express commercial with "Motormouth" John Moschitta. After awakening to the external sound of applause, I became aware of why, in my dream, the convict had spoken so fast. My brain seemed to kick the dream into high gear or shall I say, push the fast forward button, in order to meet the oncoming external stimulus. It was successful and the goal was achieved.

Summary: After careful consideration, I concluded that the speed of this dream varied so that its climax would be synchronous with the external stimulus. I further concluded that the internal mechanism which notifies the mind to begin spinning a dream to meet the future distraction had, for whatever reason, gotten off to a late start, resulting in the need to speed up the dream.

Apparently, the preparation time given to the drama society of the mind varies. And this drama society, regardless of when it is activated, is well aware of the target in time it needs to hit.

Here's the next dream which occurred at 5:14 a.m., December 4, 2001. My shorthand immediately following the dream reads, Paper hit pipe but didn't work. This jogged my memory later that morning and I wrote the following at 8:04 a.m. The dream:

A few hours ago, I awoke with the urge to urinate. I checked my watch and saw that it was already after 5 a.m. so I decided to hold off until awakening for the day since the urinal is far down the hall. I had just returned to sleep when I had a dream in which I slammed my writing pad down on the metal radiator inside my cell. This action created a sound that perfectly coincided with the sound of the metal clanking inside this particular radiator when the heat comes up. The vision of the pad hitting the metal was ridiculous since I immediately knew that paper hitting metal does not produce such a sound. I awoke with a laugh and wrote a brief description of the dream (Paper hit pipe but didn't work) so that I'd recall it in the morning.

There was apparently insufficient time to prepare a believable scenario to mimic the external stimulus. My mind seemed to settle for whatever dream props it had close at hand; my writing pad is always beside my bunk and is the first and last thing I see before falling asleep and awakening. I suspect that the dreaming brain had little time to discern what prop would work best in this scenario or it would have chosen something more appropriate like another metal object.

To sum up the two dreams recorded above: If the dreaming brain does indeed have the ability to compress a superabundant amount of material into a short period of time then the Motormouth dream should not feel raced and the radiator dream should have ample time to choose an object that would produce a more believable sound (recall cognitive ease from the last chapter). Moreover, both dreams seem to show that the dreaming brain is primarily concerned with hitting its mark with regard to the oncoming external stimuli, which offers further evidence, albeit circumstantial, of precognitive ability.

Before we move on, let's take a brief look at the history of scientific method, drop in on a meeting of the minds, and speculate as to how and why Sigmund Freud could have missed the mark with regard to Maury's dream.

Chapter Five
Eintime

It is difficult for even the most intelligent people to imagine a new idea that transcends or debunks popular thought. Although the idea that the world was round dates back to ancient times, how many people really believed it before Columbus and Magellan proved it? How many people believed that the earth was revolving around the sun before Kepler and Copernicus came along?

The history of science and exploration is rife with a courageous cast of characters who saw something their contemporaries could not see. When Galileo, who was a follower of Copernicus, said in his *Dialogue* that the sun was at the center of our universe, the church, which wanted man at the center, threatened to shove his telescope up his behind. Just joking, but in truth they took Galileo into a dungeon and showed him their instruments of torture. After taking a brief look around, Galileo said he was only kidding.

Descartes—Mr. "I think, therefore I am"—didn't have to think very long after hearing about Galileo's guided dungeon tour; he held back the two essays he was about to publish on the same subject and "I am" continued to be "I am" instead of "I was."

Luckily, threats and violence perpetrated against independent thinkers eventually grew out of fashion in the seventeenth century which is regarded by many historians as a century of genius. Aside from scientists like Galileo, there were philosophical geniuses like Francis Bacon who insisted we apply hard skepticism and systematic experiments to all of our scientific endeavors. No more shooting from the hip which so often leads civilization down the wrong path. Bacon's approach has continued to be the standard up until present day.

Sigmund Freud stepped onto the world stage at the turn of the twentieth century and dedicated his entire life to uncovering secrets that lie hidden in the deepest recesses of the human mind. But the conclusions Freud reached were hard, if not impossible to prove, as they fell outside the realm of experimentation. Freud knew he would be laughed at when he started telling the world about little people inside our heads who really control us. Luckily for Freud, there was no social media back then but his contemporaries still gave him hell. They looked around for Galileo's telescope, you know the one the church was going to shove up Galileo's behind. Except this time, Freud told everyone what the telescope's phallic shape symbolized and what shoving it up his behind would reveal about themselves. Uh-oh. A little embarrassing, you think? So they just continued to criticize him instead.

Because Freud was determined and courageous, he put up with the laughter and eventually showed everybody, or at least the consensus, that some of his ideas had merit. Although we've all gotten used to bashing Freud we mustn't forget that we are able to think in many psychological terms today because of him! Even Einstein once sent a consoling letter to Freud that read in part, "I always find it amusing to observe that even people who regard themselves as unbelievers…think and speak in your concepts the moment they let themselves go."

Anyway, now that we've jumped over to Einstein, it's a good time to point out the major difference between Freud's ideas and a proven scientific theory like $E=mc^2$. Concrete experimental methods along with math prove the latter. (Even though math is also manmade, we tend to believe figures when they add up, unless of course your business partner is also your accountant.) In Freud's own words: "I always envy the physicists and mathematicians who can stand on firm ground. I hover, so to speak, in the air. Mental events seem to be immeasurable and probably always will be so."

In contrast to mental events, the language of physics is spoken in math. This may come as a surprise to you but Albert Einstein wasn't that great in math. Sure, he was a mathematical genius compared to most people, but amongst many of his scientific colleagues, he was, eh, let's just say he needed some help every now and then. Early on in his career, while working on electromagnetism, Einstein's friend, Jakob Laub, "took over the complicated mathematical tasks, while Einstein concentrated on their physical implications." Later, while immersed in another field of physics, Einstein wrote to a friend, "I am now working exclusively on the gravitation problem and I believe that, with the help of a mathematician friend here, I will overcome all difficulties." On another occasion, when speaking about his own famous theory of relativity, Einstein wrote, "Since the mathematicians have invaded the relativity theory, I myself no longer understand it anymore."

Einstein was smart enough to consult with elite mathematicians knowing, in the world of physics, equations were necessary to support all those ingenious thoughts that were flying through his head and making his hair stand on end. He'd regularly formulate these brilliant but abstract thoughts into what is known as "thought experiments." And after methodically thinking everything out in his mind and reaching a satisfactory conclusion to each thought experiment, Einstein often recruited his dear friend, Marcel Grossmann, to help him translate his thoughts into those weird looking equations most of us have seen on a chalkboard. Einstein even had math help from his first wife, Mileva Maric, when he came up with his big whammy that changed the world, $E=mc^2$.

Luckily, for the purpose of this book, I don't have to explain to you exactly what that equation means since I barely get it myself—or at least I think I do. What I will explain here is that Einstein's theory of relativity proved that Time is relative. To illustrate this, I'll contemporize one of Professor Hair-do's analogies.

Imagine you and I are at Yankee Stadium watching the Yanks play. I'm in the nosebleed section while you're in the front row, right behind home plate. Alex "A-Rod" Rodriguez steps up to the plate, swings, and hits it out of the park. You and I are watching the same swing, and the same ball leave A-Rod's bat. But we're viewing it from two different places and distances in the stadium and therefore the moment in which it happens for each of us depends on the distance we are from home plate. So technically, even though we're both at the same game, if you want to be a smart ass and say to me afterward, "I saw A-Rod swing first," you're right. Because of the space between us, your Time and my Time are different times.

Now Einstein may have proven that this scenario is true but the idea of it was nothing new. In 1675, astronomer Olaus Roemer, while researching eclipses, realized that light takes time to travel from one region of space to another. In 1813, astronomer Sir Wilhelm Herschel told poet Thomas Campbell, a visitor to Herschel's observatory, "I have observed stars, of which the light, it can be proved, must take two millions of years to reach the earth…if those distant bodies had ceased to exist two million years ago, we should still see them, as the light would travel after the body was gone." Though Herschel's calculations were a bit off, the gist of his statement was spot-on and Einstein proved it. Everything is relative to where you are in the universe, and according to Einstein, the relativity of Time goes even deeper than this.

Now let's pretend you and I leave Yankee Stadium but in two separate cars. Before we leave, you remind me that you saw A-Rod swing first, really rubbing it in. This gloating, coupled with the fact that you had much better seats than me, leaves me a little disgruntled; my only revenge is to get home first and brag to all of our friends that I saw A-Rod swing first. I punch the pedal to the metal and leave you behind in a cloud of smoke. I hit the Brooklyn-Queens Expressway at a hundred miles per hour while you, on the other hand, putt away from the stadium coughing at one mile per hour. Einstein pointed out that the clock in my fast moving car will tick *slower* than the clock in your slow moving car. And one better, during our rides, I'll even age slower than you.

In sum, without having to get any deeper into Einstein's theories of general and special relativity, suffice it to say for the purpose of this book, that Einstein destroyed the concept of absolute Time. My Time and your Time just ain't the same Time. So I guess you can say, it's all in our heads. And on that note, let us return to Sigmund Freud who spent his lifetime getting into our heads.

Chapter Six
A Genius in Denial

Long before aspirin was invented, prehistoric men used a surgical procedure known as trepanning to bore open the human skull and relieve pressure on the brain. Eight thousand years after the earliest evidence of trepanning, Sigmund Freud bore open the human mind to relieve pressure on…the mind. In doing so, he took a dangerous step into the unknown. We are pretty demented creatures and a lot of wacky things go on in that nutshell. Even the open-minded Einstein once said, "It may not always be helpful to delve into the subconscious." But Freud was able to peel away a number of layers, sift through the mess that lay hidden in some of our darkest chambers, and help us to understand ourselves. As R.D. Laing has said of Freud, he "descended to the underworld and met there stark terrors" and we owe him eternal reverence for "the knowledge he brought back with him and conveyed to us." Numerous branches of social and behavioral sciences have stemmed from Freud's discoveries and his impact on medicine, treatment of mental disorders, even the arts and literature, can never be calculated.

The sexual deviants I have seen in prison would have provided Freud with enough observational material to last him several lifetimes. And because of Freud's work I was able to understand the hidden causes of their deviances. The journey that has led me to this book, however, is of a different nature and began with Freud's *Civilization and Its Discontents.*

    Late one night, I was in my prison cell staring at a fly that was tapping on the inside of my window; the searchlight outside was the apparent draw. I was about to get up and swat the fly when I suddenly noticed the stars flickering in the night sky. I was awestruck and a number of lofty thoughts entered my mind. I sat down and wrote the following poem:

> Here an idea my mind would try
> The universe from its farthest directions
> has an effect on the fly
> And a greater idea my mind should
> nurse
> The fly has an effect on the entire
> universe
> The furthest heavens, never to be
> unraveled
> And the infinitely small, a journey less
> traveled
> But if I can focus my mind on the latter
> Even assuming we are just matter
> The endless depths of the atom; how
> large we must be
> And the fly is no larger, nor smaller, than
> we.

    Following my little mystic moment, I put down my pen and smashed the fly. It would have otherwise annoyed me all night and I needed to sleep (a necessity this book will deal with in later chapters). So the same mind that gazed at the heavens and contemplated if Space, like Time, is an illusion, smashed a helpless fly and felt darn good about it. Gotcha! This aggression I displayed, even released in such a small dose, is one of the inherent attributes of the human mind that intrigued Freud and moved him to write *Civilization and Its Discontents*. The answers to why we swat flies—and cluster-bomb villages—are found in this work which delves into the unconscious. (To help avoid World War III, an international think tank should be formed around this work along with Gustave Le Bon's *The Crowd: A Study of the Popular Mind*.)

The brain is known as the three pound universe. At the same time Freud was trying to understand the inner workings of this mini universe, Albert Einstein was trying to answer the most puzzling questions with regard to our larger universe. These large and small universes would collide in 1927 when Freud and Einstein met for the first time in Berlin. Mr. and Mrs. Freud had traveled to Berlin to visit two of their sons and several grandchildren for Christmas. While the Freuds were staying with their son, Ernst, Einstein and his wife, Elsa, heard they were in town and dropped in on them. In this casual setting, Einstein and Freud chatted for two hours. Both men spoke German as their native tongue so they had no difficulties understanding one another. Or did they?

These two living legends had a lot in common. Both were ultra-brilliant though neither man offered any sign of genius in his youth. In fact, Freud's father once said, "The boy will come to nothing." Very similar to what one of Einstein's teachers had told Einstein's father after Dad asked what career his son should pursue. "It doesn't matter," said the teacher, "he'll never make a success of anything."

As adults, Einstein and Freud received the same dismissive treatment from their peers when discussing their new ideas. As for Einstein, many of his fellow physicists disbelieved his theories with no evidentiary basis to support their disbelief. During a visit to Gottingen where Einstein spoke of SpaceTime, student Hyman Levy (who went on to become a professor) said of certain professors attending the event, "This was all so abstract, that it became unreal to them. I remember seeing one of the professors getting up and walking out in a rage, and as he went out I heard him say, 'This is absolute nonsense.'" Freud's ideas received the same "bad reception." When Freud's theories were brought up at a 1910 congress of neurologists and psychiatrists in Hamburg, a professor "banged his fist on the table, shouting, 'This is not a topic for discussion at a scientific meeting; it is a matter for the police.'"

Besides having to contend with incredulous colleagues, Freud and Einstein had other things in common. They both enjoyed long walks alone. And both men saw through the smoke of traditional thought. I don't mean tobacco smoke but they also shared a fondness for cigars. Both men were European Jews who faced increasing anti-Semitism in their homelands as well as in their professional circles. They eventually experienced outright persecution and had to flee their native countries, Germany and Austria, to save their own lives[8].

---

[8] When Hitler seized control of Germany in March of

In their respective fields, each man came, saw, and conquered. But as smart as they were, neither man truly understood what the other had accomplished.

As for Freud's psychoanalysis, Einstein wavered between belief and disbelief but oftentimes disbelief prevailed. And not surprisingly since he couldn't even begin to understand the mind of his first wife, Mileva Maric, and offered her the monetary reward from the Nobel Prize he was expecting if she'd just give him a divorce. Nor did Einstein understand the mind of his son, Eduard, who developed an incurable mental illness before being condemned to an asylum. Einstein refused to treat Eduard with psychoanalysis even though Einstein's best friend, Michelangelo Besso, had undergone psychoanalysis and told Einstein that it mended his marriage and restored his outlook on life. Einstein may have feared that psychoanalyzing Eduard might uncover a host of paternal faults that contributed to Eduard's condition.

After losing complete contact with Eduard, Einstein wrote, "There is something blocking me that I am unable to analyze fully." Uh, hello, maybe a session in Sigmund's office could have helped; I'm sure Siggy would have freed up the sofa for an

---

1933, Einstein was abroad and publicly stated he would not return home. Freud, who originally declared, "This is my post and I can never leave it," changed his mind and fled Vienna soon after the Wehrmacht rolled into Austria. The Nazis attacked relativity and psychoanalysis, burning both men's books in a bonfire and putting a five thousand dollar contract on Einstein's head to which he replied, "I didn't know I was worth that much."

hour or so. Instead, Einstein ignored his family problems and "toward the end of his life he confessed that his strongest personal ties...had all been failures."

Einstein's aversion to psychoanalysis was matched by Freud's inability to grasp physics. When they'd met in Berlin, Freud said, "[Einstein] understands as much about psychology as I do about physics, so we had a very good conversation."

Since Freud, by his own confession, knew little or nothing about the field of physics, we can deduce that he did not understand the impact Einstein's theories had on the subject of Time. Perhaps this is the reason why Freud lends no credence to precognitive dreams in *The Interpretation of Dreams*.

In all fairness, *The Interpretation of Dreams* was published several years before Einstein published his famous theories of relativity. Yet, in seven subsequent editions of the book that were published in Freud's lifetime, or his abridged edition titled, *On Dreams*, Freud made no positive speculation as to the dreaming mind's ability to glimpse the future. Freud once remarked that the future "always reforms itself anew; even the dear Lord doesn't know it in advance." This is in stark contrast to Einstein's belief that "past, present, and future are an illusion," which would mean that the only way the dear Lord wouldn't know the future is if He's covering His eyes. In all fairness, the idea that Time is an illusion, proven by Einstein, may have been too new for Freud. (Possibly the same reason Einstein couldn't commit to psychoanalysis; too new.) The closest Freud came to the idea of timelessness was when he said, "The processes of the system [unconscious] are timeless; they are not ordered temporally, are not altered by the passage of time, in fact bear no relation to time at all."

There is another more likely reason why Freud denied the existence of precognitive dreams in *The Interpretation of Dreams*. Until Freud connected our dreams with fears and desires, people had always believed that dreams foretold the future. If the revolutionary ideas in Freud's new dream book were going to prevail over long-established beliefs, Freud knew he had to do away with traditional perspectives and he expended quite a bit of ink doing so.

After reading Freud's works, it becomes obvious that Freud deliberately shunned any ideas that might have impugned his own dream theory. When Sándor Ferenczi, Carl Gustav Jung, and other followers of Freud had asked him if they could venture into the field of occultism with both feet— not toe-dipping as they'd all done—Freud answered that "these are dangerous expeditions, and I can't go along." He feared that, if their conclusions were wrong, the venture could derail his psychoanalytic movement. Precognitive dreams are in no way the same as occultism, but either subject, considered by many as outlandish, could have toppled his already teetering psychoanalytic empire.

To further substantiate this proposition, when Ferenczi wished to give an account of his telepathic experiments at the next psychoanalytic congress, Freud replied, "I advise you against it. Don't do it…You are throwing a bomb into the psychoanalytic edifice, which will certainly not fail to explode." Surely, taking a stab in the dark at precognitive dreams would produce the same anxiety in Freud.

After a thorough badgering from his closest companions, Freud did, in the end, come around to the possibility of telepathy when he admitted to his inner circle that it "is my private affair." Were precognitive dreams also Freud's private affair? We'll never know. But we can say for sure that, whenever confronted with a dream that glimpsed the future, whether his own or those of his patients, Freud denied precognition and explained the dream away in psychoanalytic terms.

In my introduction, I said we'd bring Freud to the stand as a hostile witness. Assuming the role of prosecutor, I'll point out that Freud's psychoanalysis is a method of unleashing a patient's personal history, thus freeing that person from repressed thoughts. Why then has Freud repressed the long history of dreams which have always been thought of as portents of the future? Cannot dreams be interpreted in more ways than one? Sometimes our dreams represent fears and desires as Freud had so brilliantly taught us, yet they may also reveal glimpses of the future, which Freud categorically denied.

Inside harsher prisons, there is an unwritten rule that convicts must knock on the table before getting up to leave the chow hall. I was once in the chow hall when I was privy to a conversation in which a newjack asked a couple of old timers about the rule's origin. One of the older cons answered, "It's a respect thing. Back in the day, when prisoners weren't allowed to talk in the chow hall, this was their way of excusing themselves from the table."

The other older con offered an alternative explanation, saying, "No, that's not it! When a joint was tense and everyone was jumpy, nobody liked any sudden moves, so you knocked on the table to let everyone know you were about to get up."

The two older cons argued back and forth until I finally chimed in and said, "Why can't both of you be right?" With that, they shrugged as I knocked on the table and got up. And this outlook applies to many of the viable theories of the dreaming brain which can be thought of as many things, but never one dimensional.

In the next chapter, I'll present a number of Freud's personal dreams and allow you, dear reader, to draw your own conclusion as to Freud's degree of denial. Then we'll deal with a dream dreamt and recorded by German Chancellor Otto von Bismarck followed by an interpretation of the dream published in Freud's *The Interpretation of Dreams*.

Chapter Seven
Freud on the Fence

In this book, I assert that Freud's refusal to publicly admit that dreams may indeed have the ability to glimpse the future was politically motivated and not based on any personal conviction. To affirm my hunch, I searched for clues by reading just about every work Freud had ever published including plenty of his letters.

Let us begin with daydreaming. Just like dreaming, daydreaming is an altered state of consciousness. We all do it. In fact, as a kid, I'd sink so deep into a daydream that everything around me was blocked out and something or someone would have to yell or physically tug me back to reality. Today, we know that actual neural changes occur in the brain when we're daydreaming. And since daydreaming is so similar to dreaming, I'll begin with a daydream that Freud relates to us in his book, *The Psychopathology of Everyday Life.* In Freud's words:

"A few days after I had been awarded the title of professor—which carries considerable authority with it in countries under monarchical rule—my thoughts, while I was walking through the Inner Town, suddenly turned to a childish phantasy of revenge directed against a particular married couple. Some months earlier they had called me in to see their little daughter, who had developed an interesting obsessional symptom following upon a dream. I took a great interest in the case, whose genesis I thought I understood. My offer of treatment was however declined by her parents and I was given to understand that they thought of changing over to a foreign authority who effected cures by hypnotism. My present phantasy was that after the total failure of that attempt the parents begged me to start my treatment, saying that now they had complete confidence in me, and so on. I however answered: 'Yes, *now* you have confidence in me—now that I too have become a professor. The title has done nothing to alter my capacities; if you could not make use of me as a university lecturer you can do without me as a professor as well.'—At this point my phantasy was interrupted by a loud 'Good day to you, Professor!' and I looked up and saw walking past me the very married couple on whom I had just taken my revenge by rejecting their offer."

Aside from revealing that Freud can harbor grudges, which isn't healthy, this daydream exhibits an uncanny experience most, if not all of us, are familiar with: we're thinking of someone and suddenly the phone rings, a text or email arrives, or there's a knock at the door, and lo and behold, it's that person! Many of us might say, "I was just thinking about you" and dismiss it as coincidence. And it may be just that. Though there may also be more to it. Freud explained away his own daydreaming experience above in psychoanalytic terms, dismissing any idea that thoughts of the married couple may have been triggered by some brain impulse forewarned of the impending confrontation.

I'll now present a different example based on an interesting coincidence that occurred in Freud's life. In 1906, on Freud's fiftieth birthday, his close friends gave him the gift of a medallion. On the medallion was a passage by Sophocles, written in Greek. I'll let Ernest Jones, Freud's faithful friend and preeminent biographer, explain Freud's reaction to the gift:

"When Freud read the inscription he became pale and agitated and in a strangled voice demanded to know who had thought of it. He behaved as if he had encountered a *revenant,* and so he had. After Federn told him it was he who had chosen the inscription, Freud disclosed that as a young student at the University of Vienna he used to stroll around the great arcaded court inspecting the busts of former famous professors of the institution. He then had the phantasy, not merely of seeing his own bust there in the future, which would not have been anything remarkable in an ambitious student, but of it actually being inscribed with the *identical* words he now saw on the medallion." (Italics from the original text.)

Freud, whose life's work was to probe the deepest recesses of the human mind, surprisingly looked no deeper into the meaning of this curious incident which is far more exact in terms of detail than my own shark dream.

Granted, the two instances I cite above (the daydream and the medallion) are not precognitive dreams but in each case Freud stubbornly refused to entertain the notion of precognition and maintained that their basis lie in psychoanalysis.

Lastly, before we move on to Bismarck, I'll relate an actual dream Freud experienced while his sons were away fighting in the First World War. Before Freud dismisses this particular dream in psychoanalytic terms, he toys with the idea of it being prophetic; he prefaces his dream recollection by saying, "You will know that the connection between dreams and telepathy is commonly held to be an intimate one; I shall propound the view that the two have little to do with each other." In the very next sentence, Freud reveals his concern that new research will prove him wrong and anticipates the argument with the following defense: "And if the existence of telepathic dreams were established there would be no need to alter our conception of dreams in any way."

A few paragraphs later, Freud finally relates the dream that originally caused him to worry that one of his sons had been killed in action. He ultimately dismisses the dream as nonsense because, he writes, "My son, however, whom the dream pronounced dead, came home from the war unscathed."

Two of Freud's sons, Martin and Ernst, were both battle-hardened soldiers which gave Freud plenty of reason to worry. Jones, Freud's biographer, tells us, "Despite many hazardous adventures and hardships, his two fighting sons came safely through the war." But Jones also tells us that "Freud's *favorite sister*, Rosa, lost her *only son*, Hermann Graf, a youth of twenty, who was killed on the Italian Front." (My italics.) In reference to this family tragedy, Freud wrote to his friend, Karl Abraham, "My sister's twenty-year-old only son was killed in action. *Grief was beyond description*." (My italics.)

I'm utterly amazed that Freud made no connection between his dream and the true tragedy that came to pass. This is a man who, when using symbolism in dream interpretation, can turn just about any phallic-shaped object into a penis and any hole into a vagina, yet he could not imagine that the dream of his son's death may have foretold the untimely death of his favorite sister's only son, both of whom were serving in the same war. What was stopping Freud from making this apparent connection when we all know that juggling characters—one representing another—is a common component of our nightly dreamscape? Still, if this transference of characters is too preposterous for Freud to accept, try this one: Peter Gay, another well-known Freud biographer, writes that "a few days later, Freud discovered that on the very day he dreamt this dream, Martin was actually wounded."

In sum, Freud concludes the subject of precognitive dreams with the following words: "The notion that there is any mental power, apart from acute calculation, which can foresee future events in detail is on the one hand too much in contradiction to all the expectations and presumptions of science and on the other hand corresponds too closely to certain ancient and familiar human desires which criticism must reject as unjustifiable pretensions. I am therefore of opinion that after one has taken into account the untrustworthiness, credulity, and unconvincingness of most of these reports, together with the possibility of falsifications of memory facilitated by emotional causes and the inevitability of a few lucky shots, it may be anticipated that the spectre of prophetic dreams will disappear into nothing."

That's a pretty firm stance on the subject. But I do understand Freud's motive. Freud's radical ideas about the human psyche were difficult to defend and rendered him an outcast in the scientific community. Crossing one more line in the sand by entertaining telepathy or precognition could have blown down the house of cards he was already shielding from the wind.

Let us move on to the dream of Bismarck.

Chapter Eight
Sink the Bismarck

When we think of the word *revolution,* the mind usually calls upon scenes of military action, civil unrest, and heroic champions of a disadvantaged class. Those of us who study history may think of solitary figures like Cromwell, Robespierre, Washington, Bolivar, Mao, or Castro. But the scientific mind might take off in another direction and agree with the great historian partnership of Will and Ariel Durant who said, "The only real revolution is in the enlightenment of the mind." Having read all of Freud's works and holding him up to Will and Ariel Durant's standard of a revolutionary, Freud certainly makes my short list of distinguished scientific revolutionaries.

But even the greatest revolutionaries are only human and therefore flawed. Ironically, Robespierre couldn't stop until he sent himself to the guillotine, Cromwell's treatment of Ireland was despicable, and Mao's Cultural Revolution was one of the most violent and un-cultural episodes in human history. Likewise, character flaws are rife amongst progressive thinkers who have championed revolutions of the human mind. Voltaire and Heidegger were anti-Semitic. Emmanuel Kant did not believe that Africans possessed the same intelligence as whites, nor women the same intelligence as men. And Thomas Hobbes characterized life as "solitary, poor, nasty, brutish, and short." Not recommended reading for your depressed teenager. Finally Freud, who revealed so much to us and popularized the word repression, deliberately repressed any and all evidence that dreams could foretell the future.

Now onto Bismarck. A record of Bismarck's dream along with an interpretation is found in Freud's *The Interpretation of Dreams*. But the dream is not interpreted by Freud. Instead, Bismarck's dream is interpreted by Hans Sachs, one of Freud's most loyal followers. To give you an idea of Sachs' sycophancy toward Freud, Sachs wrote a book shortly after Freud's death titled, *Freud, Master and Friend*. As a reward for Sachs' loyalty during Freud's lifetime, Freud granted Sachs the rare privilege of becoming a full-fledged member of Freud's Committee of Six, which was a "strictly secret" committee designed "to guard the kingdom and policy of their master." Although Sachs made the cut for this secret group, we must still wonder why Freud, four hundred pages into his seminal work on dreams, suddenly hands his pen over to Sachs and allows him to interpret Bismarck's dream. On the face of it, it appears that Freud is impressed by the work of his protégé. Moreover, Sachs repeatedly credits Freud (his master and friend) with the techniques he has used to interpret Bismarck's dream; always nice to have a nod of approval from others in your field. But yet there is something deeper that has motivated Freud to include Sachs' interpretation of Bismarck's dream in his masterpiece, and it only becomes apparent after Freud's personal life is carefully analyzed. It has to do with Freud's relationship with his own father.

And as you'll see, the life of Bismarck plays a part in that relationship.

Let's first analyze Bismarck's dream and Sachs' interpretation of it, after which time we'll discuss what appears to be the true motive for its inclusion in Freud's book. To provide some relevant background, Bismarck received a letter from his royal patron and king, Wilhelm I. In the letter, the king mentions a dream he'd had and Bismarck responds with the following letter to his king:

"Your Majesty's communication encourages me to relate a dream which I had in the Spring of 1863, in the hardest days of the Conflict, from which no human eye could see any possible way out. I dreamt (as I related the first thing next morning to my wife and other witnesses) that I was riding on a narrow Alpine path, precipice on the right, rocks on the left. The path grew narrower, so that the horse refused to proceed, and it was impossible to turn round or dismount, owing to lack of space. Then, with my whip in my left hand, I struck the smooth rock and called on God. The whip grew to an endless length, the rocky wall dropped like a piece of stage scenery and opened out a broad path, with a view over hills and forests, like a landscape in Bohemia; there were Prussian troops with banners, and even in my dream the thought came to me at once that I must report it to your Majesty. This dream was fulfilled, and I woke up rejoiced and strengthened…"

Sachs makes his master proud when he fails to even entertain the possibility of precognition.

Instead, Sachs writes that the dream came to fruition because "the dreamer with whom we are concerned was not content with the fulfillment of his wish in a dream but knew how to achieve it in reality."

In other words, Bismarck's dream of conquering huge tracts of Europe and uniting various peoples into one nation is equal to fulfilling a dream of say owning a house or starting a business; simple wish fulfillment. I do understand that the degree of one's accomplishments are ordinarily parallel to an individual's abilities and level of determination, so let's consider the validity of this interpretation for a moment. After all, Bismarck was indeed a man of action who knew how to exercise his will to the extent that his own will, during his chancellorship, became synonymous with the will of greater Germany. I'll therefore try to swallow this interpretation though it does need a bit of chewing. However, a few lines later, Sachs says "that [Bismarck] took the whip in his hand was a clear allusion to masturbation." After a few paragraphs more, the entire dream is relegated to "an infantile masturbation fantasy."

I must repeat that neither Freud nor Sachs have even considered, at least in writing, that the dream—which ultimately came true—revealed a glimpse of the future. Such is obviously the conclusion Bismarck reached when he told the dream to his wife and others the next morning, and later when he related the dream to his king in the letter above.

Since I'm conducting this inquiry in the form of a trial, let's cast Bismarck in the role of a defendant as I'm sure, if alive, Bismarck would likely defend himself against allegations that his mind was engaged in "infantile masturbation fantasies" while the fate of his beloved Germany hung in the balance. Freud's book has condemned Bismarck to eternal shame so let's cross examine Freud and try to suss out if he, the witness, has any untoward feelings toward Bismarck, the defendant, which might have influenced his decision to publish this humiliating interpretation.

To begin, let's examine Freud's personal life. Freud candidly admits that "My emotional life has always insisted that I should have an intimate friend and a hated enemy. I have always been able to provide myself afresh with both." Ernest Jones adds that "[Freud] could both love and hate passionately and the one was apt to evoke the other." Erich Fromm, who wrote a number of works on Freudian psychology, echoes the sentiments above when he wrote that Freud's "friendships follow the same rhythm: intense friendship for several years, then complete break, usually to the point of hatred."

Now that we've established by Freud's own words, the words of his faithful friend and biographer, and the words of a recognized expert in the field of Freudian psychology, that it's risky to befriend Sigmund Freud, let's see if Freud's pattern of mercurial behavior toward friends has ever been projected onto men he'd never met. To do so, we'll start with a brief background into Freud's childhood.

As a child, Freud admired military heroes. He tells us that "Hannibal had a place in my phantasies" and Oliver Cromwell "had powerfully attracted me in my boyhood." Moreover, Freud can "remember sticking labels on the backs of my wooden soldiers with the names of Napoleon's marshals written on them." Nothing strange here, ordinary behavior for a boy, especially during a time when there was no Batman or Spiderman to idolize. Freud gets a little older and his attraction to military adventure continues. Jones tells us, "The Franco-Prussian War, which broke out when he was fourteen, aroused his keen interest." In comparison to the conflicts that ravaged the twentieth century, the Franco-Prussian War was a snowball fight, but there is, however, one aspect of this war worthy of note: the chancellor who instigated the war and led the Prussians (later, Germans) to victory was Otto von Bismarck.

Thus far, we've established that Freud admired great military leaders as a child and at age fourteen he became particularly interested in the Franco-Prussian War, whose glorious victor was Otto von Bismarck. Now the plot thickens.

Freud's father, Jakob Freud, was "such an ardent admirer of Bismarck...that when he had to translate the date of his birthday from the Jewish calendar into the Christian one, he chose that of Bismarck's." So father and son were both admirers of Bismarck. And Jones further points out that "there were many links between Jakob Freud and Bismarck." (Note that the man who invented the Oedipus complex, the theory in which son hates father and wishes him dead, could easily see Bismarck and his father, Jakob, rolled into one.)

After Freud grows up and becomes a doctor, we would imagine that his admiration for childhood heroes wore off; most boys outgrow their love for Spidey. Not so with Freud. Freud named his second son Oliver, after Oliver Cromwell. As for Bismarck, Jones tells us, "When the great man [Bismarck] visited Vienna [Freud's hometown] in June 1892, Freud made several attempts to see him in the flesh, but the nearest he got to it was a glimpse of his back after waiting two and a half hours in the street." Jones adds that this "behavior one would have thought very atypical of Freud." I might add, at the time of this harmless stalking spree, Freud was thirty-six years old, not fourteen.

Is it possible that Freud's disappointment in not seeing Bismarck triggered that mechanism in his mind that so easily shifts from love to hate? If this doesn't get you thinking, let's throw this into the mix. After Freud's father, Jakob, died, Freud attempted to self-analyze himself, an analysis he relates as "harder than any other." The experience motivated him to write *The Interpretation of Dreams* "as a means of getting out of a bad mood." Only after writing this book did Freud realize that the endeavor was a "reaction to my father's death." Jones traces the path of Freud's self-analysis to its conclusion, saying, "The path ended in the unexpected discovery of his deeply buried hostility to his father." A father who admired Bismarck, a father who had "many links" with Bismarck, and a father whom Freud suddenly realizes that he loathes. Such is the bitterness and hostility Freud is experiencing toward his father when he first picks up the pen to write *The Interpretation of Dreams,* which includes the interpretation of Bismarck's dream.

Jones also connects Freud's hostility toward his father with Freud's long history of destructive relationships by saying that Freud had always tried "to find a father-substitute to whom [he could] display the utmost affection, admiration, and even subservience, doubtless a repetition of an early attitude toward his father! Only, unfortunately, such false cures never succeed for long. Always the latent hostility gets transferred also, and the relationship ends…in dissension and estrangement." To place this general assessment onto a specific individual, Jones also tells us that Freud's "swelling undercurrent of hostility towards Fliess [Freud's one-time friend] was connected with the unconscious identification of him with his father." Other father-substitutes may have included one-time BFF's turned bitter enemies such as Josef Breuer, Theodor Meynert, Sándor Ferenczi, and Carl Gustav Jung, all drawn from a pool of mentors and protégés alike, which, for Freud, are two pits from the same fruit.

Now let's ponder the above. Freud may have felt rejected by Bismarck after schlepping downtown and waiting two and a half hours to see him. This disappointment alone could have marked a shift in Freud's sensitive emotions and rendered him wholly unfit to confirm or deny such an erotic and derogatory interpretation of Bismarck's dream, as given by Sachs. However, we should not discount the more likely scenario: Was Bismarck an imaginary father-substitute whom Freud spun through the same laundry cycle of love and hate as he'd done with his many other father-substitutes? When Freud's love for his own father turned to contention, while writing *The Interpretation of Dreams,* what better way to scorn him then to pull down the pants of his father's idol—whom his father admired so much that he voluntarily shared a birthday with—and let the world see him masturbating. Hey, Dad, look at your idol now! And all over the pages of a book you never thought I could write (remember Freud's dad said, "The boy will come to nothing").

Whether Freud had a direct bone to pick with Bismarck or viewed Bismarck as a substitute for his hated father, the evidence above is far too weighty to simply dismiss.

The German battleship *Bismarck* was launched in 1939 and named after Otto von Bismarck. At the time, it was one of the largest battleships ever built.

In May of 1941, two years into World War II, *Bismarck* set sail into the Atlantic Ocean to raid the Allied shipping lanes. But before she arrived there, the Brits were tipped off and British patrol ships spotted her in the Denmark Strait. The Brits engaged but didn't fare so well. *Bismarck* sunk HMS *Hood,* the Royal Navy's pride and joy, then slipped away into the open sea.

For centuries, the British Navy had mastered the seas, a courageous feat borne of necessity since the survival of their tiny island nation depended on shipping. In terms of British pride, the sinking of their beloved *Hood* was an affront that went far deeper than the *Hood's* mangled steel that now lay on the bottom of the Denmark Strait. The whole island cried out, "Sink the *Bismarck.*" After a relentless pursuit, the British Navy spotted *Bismarck* in the North Atlantic and bombarded her from air and sea; she sunk to the bottom.

In 1938, at the same time the battleship *Bismarck* was being built in a Hamburg shipyard, Freud was forced to flee Austria. Otto von Bismarck's united Germany (this time the Third Reich which followed Bismarck's Second Reich) had invaded Austria and both the Austrian and German governments persecuted Freud for being born a Jew; they arrested his beloved daughter, Anna, ran him out of town, torched his books, and sullied his name. Freud's four sisters were unable to escape the Nazis and were sent to the gas chambers at Auschwitz in 1942.

Freud died in 1939 while residing in the home I had visited in London. Had he lived to witness the short life of the battleship *Bismarck*, I imagine, given the tragic circumstances surrounding his life in the late 1930s, he'd have roared along with the rest of England when the cry went up, "Sink the *Bismarck.*" I can also imagine a sly smile etched across his old and mighty but cancerous face, knowing it was he who had fired the first salvo at the ship's namesake. Though Freud published the interpretation of Bismarck's dream four decades before the *Bismarck* was sunk, it appears that both the man and the ship were mainly targeted as the result of injured pride.

Given the above, Freud should not have published the interpretation of Bismarck's dream. But before I ask you, dear reader, to decide whether Bismarck's dream was an "infantile masturbation fantasy" or a portent of the future, we should take a brief look at Bismarck's early life—just as we'd done with Freud—then summarize his and Germany's state of affairs in the spring of 1863. This should provide you with the necessary information to make an informed decision as to the true essence of Bismarck's dream.

Chapter Nine
Missing the (Bis)Marck

Bismarck was born in April of 1815 in the fading shadow of Napoleon Bonaparte's reign. Just three years before Bismarck's birth, Napoleon, who'd conquered most of Europe, had fled Moscow on a sled, abandoning his cold starving army to the mercy of a Russian winter, an angry Russian army, and vengeful citizens. This ignominious sleigh ride marked the turning point in Napoleon's fortunes. Upon his return to France, Napoleon commented, borrowing a quote from Thomas Paine's *Age of Reason*, "There is but a step between the sublime and the ridiculous." The great Napoleon had taken that step and knew it.

Bismarck, whose beloved Germany was liberated from Napoleonic rule only on account of Napoleon's misstep, entered politics years later well aware of how easily a world leader can fall off the world stage, as did Napoleon.

Less than three months after Bismarck was born, Napoleon would not only fall off the world stage, as had happened in Moscow, but would roll down the aisle and straight out the theatre door where a cab carried him on a one-way ride from the battlefield of Waterloo to a prison on St. Helena where he died a broken man. Whether it was the snows of Russia or the muddy fields of Belgium that kicked the chair out from under Napoleon's empire, Napoleon himself knew that it all boiled down to fate when he said, "I never was truly my own master, but was always controlled by circumstances."

When Bismarck became chancellor of Germany, he'd echo Napoleon's quote about being "controlled by circumstances" by saying in his own words, "Man cannot create the current of events. He can only float with it and steer." Bismarck, like Napoleon, wanted to carve out an empire and knew that the fires he was starting in Europe could consume him as well. A little reassurance that his goals marched in step with fate would ease his anxieties and encourage him along the course he had set for himself and Germany. This reassurance would arrive in the form of the dream Bismarck dreamt and related to his king, Wilhelm I. But before we return to that dream, let's examine the geopolitical landscape of Germany at that time then see if Bismarck's dream bore any resemblance to the future.

Bismarck had been appointed prime minister in September 1862 and one of his biographers, Edward Crankshaw, tells us, "His survival was all but miraculous. He had no ministerial experience…He was a temporary disturbance, to be resisted and deplored, but not built to last." As if mere survival wasn't enough to preoccupy Bismarck's mind, he had this grand idea of unifying Germany and "revolutionizing the map of Europe." Thus, he immediately began poking around trying to find out how far he would get if he challenged Austria and its emperor, Franz Joseph, and what Napoleon III (Napoleon Bonaparte's nephew) and "the French would do if things grew hot in Germany."

Aside from these dangerous international obstacles, Bismarck ruled without a parliamentary majority in the Reichstag, and by May of 1863, the Prussian parliament was fed up with him.

Fortunately for Bismarck, he relied on King Wilhelm I for his job, not the people or parliament. But when would the king give in to the majority? If dismissed by Wilhelm I, Bismarck's career would have ended as abruptly as Napoleon's career did at Waterloo. And what if the king dropped dead? Bismarck would have to clean out his desk and start searching for a new job. In fact, years later, when Wilhelm II inherited the reigns of Germany from his father, Wilhelm I, Little Willy dismissed Bismarck as casually as a master might do away with a menial servant who has failed to run a bath at the correct temperature. For these and other reasons, Bismarck, aka the Iron Chancellor, "came to realize that European politics could not be forced into a pattern even by a man of ruthless will."

And here we come to Bismarck's dream in the spring of 1863. When Bismarck went to sleep that night he could only hope that his self-appointed mission to unite Germany would fit into history's larger purpose. If so, the outrageous odds against him would mean nothing. If not, he's doomed. Here is Bismarck's dream with my own interpretation:

"In the spring of 1863," Bismarck finds himself "in the hardest days of the Conflict, from which no human eye could see any possible way out." He goes to sleep and dreams he is on an "Alpine path with a precipice on the right, rocks to the left." If you look at a map of Europe and imagine the Alps as a mountain chain across the top of Italy,

France (and its leader Napoleon III) would sit at the left of this chain, and Austria (and its leader Franz Joseph) to the right, with Germany at the center. If Bismarck started out in Germany and rode a horse straight into the Alps then France would be on his right and Austria to his left. Either way you look at it, Bismarck is hemmed in by what he sees as two enemies.

"The path grew narrower." Things were getting worse.

"The horse refused to proceed." This appears to be the stubborn old king, Wilhelm I, who always needed a good whipping into action from Bismarck. Interestingly, anyone familiar with the era can imagine Bismarck holding the reins of King Wilhelm I. Recall that Sachs had insisted that Bismarck was the horse, an ill-researched and erroneous connection as you'll now see. A bit of research into Bismarck's life clearly shows that Bismarck thought of the king—not himself—as a horse, which happens to lend further credence to Bismarck's own interpretation of his dream. Three of Bismarck's biographers also maintain this view. A.J.P. Taylor writes that Bismarck "compared the king to a *horse* who takes flight at an unaccustomed object, will grow obstinate if driven, but will gradually get used to it." Erich Eyck echoed Taylor's quote when he wrote, "[Bismarck] compared the king with a *horse* that shied at every new object and became restive and unmanageable if one tried force, but would get accustomed to it little by little." Lastly, Edward Crankshaw writes, "In June 1866, on the very eve of war, [Bismarck] declared to the Hungarian rebel General Stefan Turr,

'I have not yet succeeded in convincing the king that war is immediately necessary, but never mind, I have put the *horse* at the ditch and he must jump.'" If Bismarck had deciphered this symbolism, he did not share it with the king, rather prudently I might add, as the king would not have appreciated being thought of as a horse.

"It was impossible to turn around." The conflict was past the point of return, or Bismarck's own pride and will forbade him to retreat.

"Or dismount." He's stuck with this king, like it or not; a reoccurring theme during Bismarck's reign.

"Owing to a lack of space." Bismarck obviously feels constricted as his path narrows.[9]

"Struck the smooth rock." The smooth rock may refer to Franz Joseph or more likely Napoleon III, who Victor Hugo referred to as "Napoleon le Petit," as opposed to Napoleon III's short but towering uncle, Napoleon I, who Hugo referred to as "Napoleon le Grand." I'm certain Bismarck was relieved to know that III could not fit into I's boots. By 1866, Bismarck's Prussian troops had crushed Austria at the Battle of Koniggratz. By 1870, Bismarck's Prussian troops, supported by Bavarian troops, encircled the French army at Sedan, trapping

---

[9] Lack of space remained a core German problem throughout the latter part of the nineteenth and first half of the twentieth centuries. In his autobiography, *Mein Kampf,* Adolf Hitler uses the term "lebensraum," or "living space," to stir up nationalist feelings that Germany was boxed in and entitled to more land. Hitler's invasion of the East, a debacle that probably cost Germany the war, was attributed, aside from Hitler's desire to crush the "Bolshevik menace," to his search for lebensraum.

them in a pincer movement. Whether the "smooth rock" was Franz Joseph or Napoleon III, both men and their respective nations had been "struck" and defeated.

At this point in the dream, Sachs makes an interesting observation by pointing out the connection between Bismarck, who "struck the smooth rock" and "calls on God," to Moses who did the same in the Bible's book of Exodus. Sachs writes: "The whole episode of a miraculous liberation from need by striking a rock and at the same time calling on God as a helper bears a remarkable resemblance to the Biblical scene in which Moses struck water from a rock for the thirsting Children of Israel. We may unhesitatingly assume that this passage was familiar in all its details to Bismarck who came of a Bible-loving Protestant family. It would not be unlikely that in this time of conflict Bismarck should compare himself with Moses, the leader."

Well, I couldn't agree more with Sachs' assertion, but while I'm still nodding my head in agreement, Sachs muddies the water with the following paragraph:

"But on the other hand the Bible passage contains some details which apply well to a masturbation phantasy. Moses seized the rod in the face of God's command and the Lord punished him for this transgression by telling him that he must die without entering the Promised Land. The prohibited seizing of the rod (in the dream an unmistakably phallic one), the production of fluid from its blow, the threat of death—in these we find all the principal factors of infantile masturbation united."

I can only shake my head at this while Freud obviously nodded his head. Anyway, continuing with Bismarck's dream:

"The whip grew to an endless length." Like any person with infinite ambition, there is no end to Bismarck's dreams of conquest.

"The rocky wall dropped like a piece of stage scenery." The seemingly insurmountable obstacles were easily removed as France and Austria were defeated.

In conclusion, I do agree that the motivation to become a world leader can stem from character deficiencies, grave disappointments in childhood, and *terribly repressed sexual urges*, though I strongly disagree with Sachs' interpretation which was endorsed by Freud. I am not a fuddy-duddy who cannot imagine sexual symbolism sprinkled into a dream of greater purpose. But if Bismarck's dream does indeed contain sexual symbolism then it is because sex and history walk hand in hand. The history of the human race cannot proceed without sex; one cannot be torn from the other, as Minkowski has said of Space and Time, "A type of union of the two will stand independently on its own." Dreams also have both threads—sex and history—running through their cloth, as do waking minds, but I find it hard to give the whole dream up to sex when its deeper meaning is blatant, has come to fruition, and is therefore endorsed by history.

Very few of us have been immersed in an international crisis such as the one Bismarck found himself in at the time. Most of us, however, have been in critical situations which demand our every last whit of attention. Personally speaking, the very last thing on my mind would be sex, even if my libido has been bottled up for some time. Though sex would probably come to mind immediately following a resolution to the problem at hand, and may very well return with a vengeance that demands extra attention, it would not rule supreme in my dreams but at best share center stage with, or accept a secondary role to, my mind's search for a solution to the crisis. To bolster my argument with neurophysiological evidence, *The Oxford Companion to the Mind* states that, "in anxiety ridden dreams there is loss of the usual penile erections."

The waking mind must constantly juggle between primitive instincts and higher ideals like careers and raising children. A constant conflict arises between who we want to be and who we need to be, what we want to do and what we need to do. Do we skip work today and go to the beach? In Bismarck's case, he had to figure out if what he wanted was also what was best—or destined—for Germany. And his dilemma was not as easy as work vs. beach. Bismarck's dream may have been one part of the mind telling another—or his brainstem telling his cortex—to steam forward and press on without reservation. This is the same exact effect my shark dream had on me. At that time, I needed to forget the adverse decision from the court, sweep away all my bitterness, block out the raucous violence and sexual perversions teeming around me, and sink into my books where the keys to my future lie. After that shark dream, I gave myself a relentless regimen, missing sleep and meals, and poring through thousand-page books as fast as someone reads a love letter. And it would not have mattered if another person thought or felt my dream was true or not; I believed it was true and that's what mattered since the dream succeeded in pushing me forward toward my destiny. A dream is wholly subjective, it is one part of our mind communicating with another, and it is best assessed by the impact it has on the dreamer. In my case, I was spurred on by my own interpretation, an interpretation derived from the same mind, albeit a different layer, as the mind that had sent it. Bismarck was convinced that his dream had foretold the future, a reassurance that pushed him forward "in the hardest days of the Conflict from which no human eye could see any possible way out." A nod such as this, even from a dream, is all a highly driven person may need to dig down deep and plow forward against all odds, and in turn, meet his or her destiny. Because Bismarck drew this conclusion from the dream and stuck to his guns, quite literally, may be the reason why his dream did indeed come to fruition. History had masterfully maneuvered him into its larger purpose.

I now arrive at the ultimate goal of these past two chapters. Freud's refusal to credit Bismarck's dream with any insight into the future renders him utterly ill-equipped to examine the illusion of Time in relation to Maury's dream. A detective who refuses to admit that men are capable of murder cannot investigate a homicide!

Chapter Ten
Sleep AID

In previous chapters, I presented overwhelming evidence that Freud deliberately ignored or explained away precognitive dreams. This neglect or denial can be viewed as a minor offense in the overall history of science had Freud's pioneering work on dreams not kick-started an entire field of dream research that, for the most part, has also disregarded the strong possibility that dreams can foretell the future.

The scientific rules laid down during the Enlightenment prohibit scientists from speculating without hard evidence. As Einstein said, "Belief that did not itself rest on knowledge was superstition, and as such had to be opposed." However, I'm convinced I can offer enough evidence to jump start a fresh scientific inquiry into precognitive dreams.

Most of the dreams I recorded in prison were variations of the stop sign dreams I had experienced in my youth. And I've concluded that all such dreams are designed with the primary purpose of impeding my ability to distinguish between the noise in my dream and the external stimuli. After experiencing the Motormouth dream detailed in Chapter Four, I was on the alert for similar dreams that also altered the dream's pace. Though these dreams occurred infrequently, they did suggest that the drama society of the mind had more or less time to prepare for the oncoming external stimuli. Sometimes the production and timing was

brilliant, worthy of an Academy Award. Other times
the dream felt rushed and shoddy, proving that the
mind does not have the ability, for example, to recite
the complete works of Shakespeare in the flash of a
second as the commentaries of Freud and others
might suggest, and many contemporary scientists
continue to propose.

The following dreams represent another
milestone in my thought process. Quite significantly,
I recorded these particular dreams on the morning
after they had occurred as opposed to awakening
during or immediately after a dream and recording
the content right away. As you'll see, I was fortunate
to remember each dream hours later. But my
inability to wrestle myself awake during the dream
or immediately thereafter was the key to exposing an
additional insight, an insight which revealed the
dream's primary purpose.

The first dream:

I was standing beside a table having a
conversation with another inmate. The
conversation seemed to carry on a bit before I
lifted a heavy bag from the floor and dumped
the contents of the bag onto the table. Though I
do not recall or am unaware of what was in the
bag, the items that fell out caused a number of
clings and clangs. The noises in my dream
perfectly corresponded to a series of noises
outside my cell. It seemed some objects were
either intentionally dumped out onto a hard
surface or had accidentally fallen. Although the
sounds were disturbing enough to stir me in my
sleep, at which time I clearly realized my
dream's design, I was utterly unable to rouse

myself from total sleep and record the dream. I felt as if I was paralyzed. I desperately tried to muster the will to rise so I could record the dream, reminding myself, in this half-sleep, that I'd likely forget it in the morning. I ultimately lost the battle with myself and fell back to sleep. Fortunately, I now recall the dream and I feel the recollection is due to the battle I had waged within myself. I speak as though there were two different people at odds inside me, and this is exactly how I felt.

As you can see, a semiconscious part of me had fought with an unconscious part of me and lost, which indicates to me how strong the unconscious desire is to remain asleep. It is therefore easy to imagine the great lengths the unconscious mind will go to in order to keep a sleeper sleeping. This may seem obvious to many but to me, at the time, it revealed the primary purpose of these dreams.

The second dream:

I had just dozed off and experienced a dream in which Rodee (a fellow con) and I were outside by the compost pile. We were standing beside a pull-up bar he and I had just built. I thought the apparatus was well built while Rodee was expressing concerns over its durability. He and I went back and forth with this until one of us suggested we test it. Rodee then kicked the platform of the structure causing a noise that perfectly corresponded with a loud noise outside of my cell. I became aware of the external stimulus and was amused by my dreaming mind's ability to blend it so seamlessly into my dream. Interestingly, I wasn't at all startled by this loud noise that should have otherwise roused me from sleep. I wanted to rise and record the dream but couldn't. It is now morning and I am remembering this dream, probably due to the loud noise.

Just like the last dream, I feel the primary purpose of this dream was to keep me asleep.

The third dream:

I was in my earliest stages of sleep when I began to experience a dream in which I was on the roof of a small building, looking down. I was holding a rope tied to a bucket and swinging the bucket between two sets of scaffolding. (This dream imagery was similar in appearance to the small construction site I now pass daily on my way to the compost pile.) My intent in the dream was to swing the bucket against a lower window in order to break the window. I tried several times without success, the bucket either falling too short of its mark or hitting the glass with insufficient force to shatter it. Finally, just as the final blow from the bucket broke the glass, an identical noise from the external environment penetrated my sleep. But instead of being startled awake, I was rather pleased, having broken the window in my dream which is to say, I accomplished my intent. (I may have also experienced a petty satisfaction, having destroyed the property of my captors, something I could not and would not do in reality.) Following, or in the midst of this cheap thrill, I recognized the loud external stimulus as the true source of the noise in my dream.

Is it possible that my dreaming brain had created internal preparations for the loud external stimulus about to occur in order to save me from having to experience the startling effect this same noise would have otherwise caused me? I could not rise and record the dream as sleep had a firm hold of me. It seems I struck a compromise with my unconscious and was able to force myself to repeat "remember the bucket dream" several times aloud before sinking back into a deep sleep. I relate it now and I commend my sleeping mind for its brilliant production—and for keeping me asleep!

There is an afterthought that did not occur to me at the time I recorded my concluding thoughts above but only dawned on me while writing this book. I originally categorized this last dream as one that successfully kept me asleep but now I have also taken note that the bucket only broke the window after several attempts. Why did it take several attempts? Was the dreaming brain performing a similar function to the Motormouth dream but in reverse? Instead of speeding up the pace, the dreaming brain may have been stalling for time while waiting for the external stimulus to arrive. In contrast to the Motormouth dream, the bucket dream had plenty of preparation time. Dreams mirror real life. In real life, sometimes we're prepared and arrive at our destinations early, while other times we run late and must rush to get there.

During each of the three dreams noted above, I cannot say if I was more tired than usual but

I was in the earlier stages of sleep and each dream succeeded in keeping me asleep. I'm pretty sure, had I not been keen to recall my dreams, I'd have never known these dreams had occurred. This makes me wonder how many times a night the dreaming mind tricks us into believing that a loud, external sound is only part of a dream so that we can remain asleep, uninterrupted. Many of us are familiar with the ringing telephone that also rings in our sleep as part of a dream. Sometimes we wake up while other times we sleep through the distraction; it may depend on our state of mind at the moment. Do we want to be bothered or not? Are we expecting a call? Are we worried about a loved one?

The bottom line is that sleep is essential. And the brain is tasked with the job of keeping us in that state, even if that means glimpsing the immediate future and preparing for it. Freud has said, "Dreams are guardians of sleep." How difficult, moreover impossible, would sleep be if the dreaming brain let its guard down?

While being transferred from one prison to another I've suffered from sleep deprivation and it is torture. Even minimal distractions that sheer away minutes of sleep over the course of a night contribute to an unhealthy sleep regimen that negatively affects every aspect of our waking lives. Without this dreaming mechanism in place, which I'll refer to henceforth as *Anticipatory Incorporation Dreams*, or *Sleep AID*, many of us might seldom, if ever, experience the comfort of a sound night's sleep and may actually go mad from loss of sleep. Each morning we'd rise from beneath the sheets as though crawling out from under the rubble of a train wreck.

In sum, the dreams noted in this chapter kept me asleep against my own will, but in doing so awakened me (pun intended) to the dream's primary purpose: to filter out interruptions and keep me asleep. Moreover, the delayed climax of the bucket dream lends even more credence to the anticipatory nature of these particular dreams; it appears that, now and then, the unconscious is well aware of what is about to happen in the external world.

Chapter Eleven
Off with the Head! Or a Broken Bed?

As illustrated in the last chapter, *Sleep AID* may be a primordial design hardwired into our brains to disguise distractions that might otherwise wake us and disrupt our sleep. To do so, *Sleep AID* must identify the external stimuli before it arrives in the present moment.

We all know the dangers involved with sleep loss. Well, one night, before I had gone to prison, I had experienced a bad night's sleep and the following day, while driving on an expressway with my girlfriend, I fell asleep at the wheel. We were traveling at the top end of the speed limit when my car went straight into a row of plastic construction barrels. Had one of those barrels been a tree or an immovable object, we both could have been killed in the accident. This incident serves as a perfect example in which my own survival and that of another human being was dangerously compromised by a lack of sleep. Sadly, there are countless tragedies that do not end so harmlessly.

Aside from keeping us asleep, *Sleep AID* may also prevent shock. We've all heard people say, "You nearly scared me to death!" This does in fact happen; plenty of people have died from shock. And this calls to mind the dream of Maury which presents us with a perfect example of an extreme situation that rates much higher than a sleep interruption. In Maury's guillotine dream, *Sleep AID*

did not succeed in keeping Maury asleep but did a
fine job of easing him through the ordeal.

To explain how, I'll first rewind back to my
teen years. Back then, I had been involved in gang
fights and I've seen men hit square across their
heads with baseball bats. Regrettably, I've hit a few
men myself. And amazingly, no one died. The
ability to withstand a blow during these fights was
not the exception but the rule. Yet, on one occasion
that did not involve a gang fight, my friends and I
were hanging out in a schoolyard when one friend
lobbed a basketball at another. The young man at the
receiving end was not looking, and although he was
a sturdy guy, when the ball hit him in the head, it
knocked him out cold. As he dropped to the ground,
I was astonished. How could so many men withstand
so many blows from aluminum or wooden baseball
bats, yet an air-filled rubber ball sent a tough young
man to the ground for the count? Besides karma, the
only answer I arrived at was this: the men struck by
the baseball bats were prepared for the blows and
were able to brace themselves, body and mind, for
the impact. In contrast, my friend who was hit by the
basketball was caught unawares. With no split-
second warning to prepare, he suffered the
consequences.

Thus, in the case of Maury, we must ask
ourselves if the blow from the bed frame was less
harmful to him because of his dream than it would
have otherwise been had his mind, albeit his
dreaming mind, been wholly unprepared. As Maury
approached the guillotine and was bound to the
plank by the executioner, his mind was preparing
him for the blow. And this preparation, similar to

that of a man who sees a baseball bat being swung at his head, may have spared Maury from worse damage to his spinal cord.

One might rightly argue that he who is guillotined is worse off than one whose bed frame has broken beneath him. But can we honestly compare the two? To be guillotined in a dream is far less dangerous than an actual blow to one's cervical vertebrae. And just imagine the damage that blow can cause when caught entirely off-guard. Such an impact can leave someone paralyzed or dead. To boot, Maury was not only prepared for the blow, but may have awoke relieved to find that his head was still on his shoulders and not being raised before a cheering crowd of bloodthirsty lunatics. "That's it? I'll get over that. For a moment, I thought I was dead."

Still, we must ask ourselves why the dream did not simply warn and wake Maury, and prevent the incident altogether. Though I cannot answer this question in the case of Maury, the general answer is that it sometimes does. For example, I was in prison with a man who was sent to solitary confinement for disciplinary reasons. The solitary confinement unit was overcrowded and each con was forced to bunk with another con. The con whom I knew was placed in a cell with a fellow gang member of a man he'd once stabbed. The two men made small talk and the con I knew had no idea that his new cell mate had recognized him. The con I knew went to sleep. At some point, he suddenly awoke with his cell mate standing over him, holding a knife. When telling me the story, he assured me that he did not hear or feel anything that alerted him, and had no idea why he had opened his eyes at that very moment. But because he did, he was able to thwart the knife attack and save his own life. Although I have been told other stories similar to this one, I reserve judgment since they are second-hand and I have not experienced the same myself so cannot hold them up to severe scrutiny. I relate them only to provoke thought.

Having just written about someone who was nearly stabbed, it's a good time to recap a period in history when nearly an entire nation gave in to a false rumor that they had been stabbed in the back, a rumor that is relevant to this book as it happened to impact the lives of Einstein and Freud. I'll then speak of a time when I personally believed I was stabbed in the back, certain the neurological mechanism behind my theory of *Sleep AID* had failed me.

Let us begin with the story of Germany in the wake of World War I.

Chapter Twelve
A Stab in the Back

In November 1918, while Albert Einstein was living in Berlin and Sigmund Freud was living in Vienna, the German nation capitulated to the Allied powers after four long years of what was then called the Great War, better known today as World War I.

At the time of Germany's surrender, the German Army was short on reserves and utterly exhausted. But the fact that the German military had already "destroyed the Tsar's army, trounced the Italians and Romanians, demoralized the French and, at the very least, denied the British a clear cut victory," led many in the German military to ask why and how the politicians back home had suddenly surrendered. The uber-proud military was not about to accept responsibility for this humiliating defeat. To boot, the unconditional terms of surrender, or Diktat, which were imposed by the Allies, made the defeat all the more shameful.

In charge of Germany at the time, at least in name, was Wilhelm II, that snot-nose kid who gave Bismarck the boot. All grown up now, he was known to the world as Kaiser Wilhelm (thanks to Bismarck who made his dad an emperor). Kaiser Wilhelm was also quick to deflect responsibility for Germany's defeat, blaming civilian politicians in Berlin. One condition of Germany's surrender was that the Kaiser would have to step down, a demand to which he replied, "I wouldn't dream of abandoning the throne because of a few hundred Jews and a thousand workers." Aside from this ill-conceived finger pointing, the Kaiser grossly underestimated the forces against him; by this time, he "had degenerated into a minor player in whom no one had any interest other than somehow to get him off the stage." Recall how I pointed out earlier in this book that Bismarck knew how easily a world leader can tumble and fall. Well, another one gone! Little Willy was shoved onto a train bound for Holland where he officially abdicated; the throne of Germany was kaput and a lot of outdated monarchical traditions went with it. Had the famous writer and veteran of the First World War, Robert Graves, bid him farewell at the station, Graves might have waved to Willy and said, "Good-bye to all that."

Wilhelm lived out his days in bitter exile while back home in Germany, silly replaced Willy. The silly belief, that is, that Germany had been stabbed in the back by traitors who signed the armistice; the German people labeled them the "November Criminals" in reference to the month of the surrender. But a handful of politicians couldn't bear all the blame so the defeated Germans began to also denounce Catholics, pacifists, communists, socialists, liberals, and Jews. As a result of this blame-campaign, Adolf Hitler rose to power while promising to do away with Germany's internal enemies, especially Jews.

Einstein, sounding more like Freud, described Germany's condition after Hitler's rise as "a state of psychic distemper in the masses." Soon, all hell broke loose and the systematic genocide that followed can be classified as the most regrettable moment in humankind's "long succession of useless cruelties."

To imagine the shocking descent of the traditionally brilliant German mind at this time, historians often highlight the cowardly and infamous acts of political or military brutes, but to keep in line with the theme of this book let's take a peek at Germany's elite scientific establishment, many of whom were eager to jump onto the Nazi bandwagon of racial supremacy.

The director of the institution at Dresden said, "Modern physics is an instrument of Jewry for the destruction of Nordic science. True physics is the creation of the German thought." German physicist and Nobel laureate Johannes Stark "became a bitter doctrinaire critic of Einstein and his works." Stark "advocated the view that there was something 'un-German'" about Einstein's theories and if "German physicists accepted the relativity theory even though it was repugnant to the German spirit," it must be because they have "Jewish wives." Even Carl Gustav Jung, Freud's former friend and protégé, joined in the fray. Along with Matthias Heinrich Göring (cousin of Reichsmarschall Hermann Göring), Jung edited a journal called the *Zentralblatt fur Psychotherapie*. Jung's "chief function was to discriminate between Aryan psychology and Jewish psychology, and to emphasize the value of the former."

In all, over a dozen Nobel laureates and nearly half of Germany's professors of theoretical physics were forced to flee the country. The making of the atomic bomb is an indirect result of this unconscionable inhospitality toward these scientists. Though Einstein did not invent nor directly participate in the actual development of the bomb, his equation, $E=mc^2$, did establish the possibility of energy (E) being released from mass (m). That possibility was useful to other physicists who honed in on the uranium nucleus as a good candidate for this reaction due to the extreme fission within its nucleus. One such physicist was a brilliant woman by the name of Lise Meitner, who was also forced to flee Germany. While walking in the snowy woods of Copenhagen with her nephew Robert Frisch, another refugee, Lise and Robert figured out that the uranium nucleus was so overstuffed with neutrons, like a fat man's belly stuffed with macaroni, that one more noodle, or neutron, would blow it apart.

Enrico Fermi, an Italian physicist and refugee who fled Fascist Italy along with his Jewish wife, figured out how to insert that additional force into the nucleus. Leo Szilard, another physicist and German refugee, approached Einstein with this new information, relying on Einstein's worldwide reputation to get the refugees' findings to U.S. President Franklin D. Roosevelt so something could be done to unleash this energy before Nazi scientists beat them to the punch. So at least five refugees, Meitner, Frisch, Fermi, Szilard, and Einstein, were instrumental in the Allies attainment of the atomic bomb.

When Max Planck, famous for quantum theory (to be discussed briefly in the Epilogue), tried to dissuade Hitler from implementing his anti-Jewish policies, Hitler responded, "If the dismissal of Jewish scientists means the annihilation of

German science, then we shall do without science for a few years!" I wonder if Hitler remembered these words when he was hiding in a bunker like a rat in a hole, hoping for a super weapon. Nonetheless, the story of these refugees provides an ideal cautionary tale with regards to the conduct of nations toward its minority citizens.

Moving along, when Freud and Einstein had met on that fateful day in Berlin I'd spoken of earlier in this book, it was a direct result of the stab-in-the-back myth which escalated into Kristallnacht, which morphed into the Final Solution, which ended with fifty-five million dead and a concrete wall dividing Germany for decades. The carnage that resulted from this myth should teach us to always beware of rumors. On occasion, we truly are betrayed or stabbed in the back while oftentimes accusations are hurled without basis. And this brief history of a tragedy that began with a false accusation brings me back to my dream theory and the feeling that I was stabbed in the back.

As the purpose of *Sleep AID* began to take shape, I developed a faith in it similar to the faith we have in our body to keep pumping blood and breathing without voluntary action. After all, I was sure that *Sleep AID* was responsible for guarding my sleep during loud nights in the most chaotic prisons, in turn preserving my mental and physical health. However, this newfound faith was shattered one night. I'll relate how as it appears in my notes.

The dream:

Someone violently kicked my steel locker. I awoke startled. It's an attack. Must fight. Defend self. Up and out of bed. Fists clenched. Heart thumping. I felt an adrenaline rush. Still feel it. Fight or flight was activated.

Turns out to be a guard who told me he has the wrong con then stormed out of my cell. I nearly struck him. My body is still in overdrive as I sit on my bunk. My heart is racing. I now come around to the question: Why didn't dream (now *Sleep AID*) warn me?

Until that night, *Sleep AID* seemed to work perfectly. Now I questioned the theory and wondered if I was wasting my time. After all, if I was so sure that *Sleep AID* was designed to shield us from distractions, ease us through a startling ordeal, or prevent shock, why had it failed me so miserably?

Over the following nights and weeks to come, *Sleep AID* resumed its normal behavior though I continued to think about why it had failed me on the night the guard had stormed into my cell. If the dreaming brain can indeed glimpse the future, as I had supposed, then the long corridor the guard had walked to get to my cell should have allowed my dreaming brain plenty of time to prepare for the event and in turn ease the jolt I had received, which caused an unnecessary activation of my fight or flight response.

Then one night, a few weeks after this problem first arose, I was startled awake by a knife fight outside my cell. One of the knife-wielding men screamed, and it seemed, as I opened my eyes, that the fight was right on top of me. In actuality, the men were just outside my doorway but too close for comfort. I recalled no dream and again questioned *Sleep AID*. I began to question this second failure along with the first.

After draining my brain, I finally admitted to myself that it was best to move on to other things unless an explanation presented itself. The very same night I decided to move on, I went to sleep and awoke with the following thoughts:

I have just been struck with a possible explanation as to why, on the night the guard had violently kicked my locker, [*Sleep AID*] had failed me. In all of the dreams I had recorded until then, I was never the object of a direct threat from the source of the external stimulus. In the case of the knife fight, as in the case of the guard, I was confronted with an external threat.

Why would my mind wish to disguise a real threat? The answer is that it would not. [*Sleep AID*] has not failed me but deliberately refrained from intervening, or was not activated.

In conclusion, if something in the external environment poses a true threat, the danger in the natural world must take precedence over sleep so that the threat can be faced and dealt with, possibly defended against. Thus, in both the case of the knife fight and the prison guard, who also seemed out for blood, the dreaming mind did not fail me but identified a real threat in the natural world and either did not activate, or purposely disarmed [*Sleep AID*], so that I could confront the threat. It appears that the dreaming mind can distinguish between a potential interruption and a true threat. This did surprise me at first but upon further thought my conscious mind must distinguish between the two as a means of survival all day long in prison, and my unconscious mind seems to be far more intelligent, discerning, and insightful than my conscious mind. I imagine that's why most of our problems are solved while we're asleep, including this one!

Chapter Thirteen
Two Slices of Bacon to Start the Day

We've all heard that a healthy breakfast is good for the mind. I don't believe that would include bacon. But there are two slices of bacon that are super healthy for the scientific mind: Roger Bacon and Francis Bacon.

Living in the 1300s, Roger Bacon was far ahead of his time. He contemplated microscopes and telescopes before they were officially invented, and his "experimental science" that allowed for "two modes of acquiring knowledge...reasoning and experience," was also an approach that was ahead of his time.

A couple of hundred years after Roger Bacon died, Francis Bacon (no relation to Roger) continued to advocate reasoning and experience and "the art of logic" as the true means of approach to science. The lives of these two Bacons were quite similar, right down to the fact that they'd both done a little jail time, a good place to think.

Albert Einstein can be considered a disciple of these Bacons. He once told a reporter, "As a boy of twelve...I was thrilled in seeing that it was possible to find out truth by reasoning alone." Many years later, this big-brained boy had grown up but still swore by reasoning and experience. "All knowledge of reality starts from experience and ends in it," he once told a lecture hall at Oxford.[10]

---

[10] Einstein's faith in reason may have originated from

Until I had learned that reasoning and experience were Einstein's big secrets, I had imagined him in a lab with a beaker in his hand as clearly as I can see a hillbilly with a beer can. Not so. As for lab experiments, Einstein had "fears regarding the laboratory" and wouldn't "pick up a piece of apparatus for fear it might blow up." No lab coat, no smoking beakers for Einstein who probably knew less about a laboratory than the crooked but helpful science teacher I'd met in jail. But Einstein knew the power of reasoning and experience. He was a thinker, plain and simple.

At some point during my incarceration, I found myself lying on my back on a patch of grass in a prison yard, thinking. I had just put down the book I was reading when I stared up at the clear blue sky in awe. Although my life had been pretty miserable until then, I had discovered books in prison and had read over a thousand of them. To me, each book was a trophy, so I guess I felt like some sort of biblio-champion. However, it suddenly dawned on me that although books had widened my knowledge, the bulk of my intellectual evolution was derived from experience, reasoning, and observing the world around me. My own

German philosopher Emmanuel Kant who wrote *Critique of Pure Reason* which posited reason and experience together as one. Max Talmey, a friend of the Einstein family, tells us, "I recommended to [Einstein] the reading of Kant. At the time, he was still a child, only thirteen years old, yet Kant's works, incomprehensible to ordinary mortals, seemed clear to him."

surroundings, even in prison, offered endless clues as to the sublime perfection of our world. The sun rises and sets. The moon moves the tides. The clouds water the soil which grows food that nourishes the body. I guess I'd spotted what Einstein called, "The beautiful harmony of the structure of this world." Sure there were also gun towers, high stone walls, and coils of razor wire around me, but these crude monuments only reinforced my firm belief that the world was a just place. I had acted the savage and could not complain when I was in turn treated like one. But the fact that I realized my faults and was working on correcting them also seemed an important part of our perfect world.

While lying on that prison lawn, I plucked a blade of grass and viewed it as a single thread in the fabric of the universe. On the inside cover of the book I had been reading I wrote the following words:

> Teachers and tutors
> Sages and savants
> Books to make the witless weep
> From all these knowledge may seep
> But if you seek wisdom not found in a class
> You may pluck from the ground, and twirl around
> A single blade of grass.

Now I know I'm no poet as I'm sure you've already gathered from my fly poem earlier in this book. But seeing the wisdom of the universe all around me, and appreciating the intense solitude I had to think about it, turned the curse of my imprisonment into a mixed blessing.

Albert Einstein did not have to go to prison to appreciate solitude. All day long he'd look for places where he could think, uninterrupted. He'd sit around and doodle, play the violin, or listen to some classical music, all the while thinking and pursuing a problem to its end. He'd even hike alone in the Alps, or sail alone on a lake where "people could not easily reach him." But now and then Al would roll the rock away from the entrance to his cave and seek out bright minds to bounce his ideas off of. Sure, after he'd become a big shot he'd converse with other notable geniuses like Ernst Mach, Madame Curie, and Max Planck. But while Einstein was still a little shot, working a menial, boring job at a patent office, he'd run his thoughts by Michelangelo Besso and Josef Sauter, two ordinary yet extraordinary pals he'd walk to and from work with.[11] Even Einstein's

---

[11] After graduating from the Zurich Polytechnic Institute, Einstein tried to find a job or secure an assistant's position at a university. The letters he and his father wrote to this end reveal a begging desperation to be given just a chance to show his talent and nothing more. After a string of rejections, Marcel Grossmann came to the rescue recommending Einstein for a menial job at the Bern Patent Office.

Toward the end of Einstein's life, he wrote that this was "the greatest thing Marcel Grossmann did for me as a friend." Next, Einstein urged Besso to work there as well. "By being deliberately critical, Besso helped Einstein sharpen his concepts." Einstein closes his 1905 paper on relativity with the words: "In conclusion, I wish to say that in working at the problem here dealt with I have had the loyal assistance of my friend and colleague M. Besso, and that I am indebted to him for several valuable suggestions."

first wife, Mileva Maric, helped him with his theory of relativity. (A Jew and a Slav, two of Hitler's favorite sub-humans; their genius must have really burned Hitler's ass. I love it when history has a sense of irony.)

As I hope I've conveyed in previous chapters, by relying on experience and reason, I have taken the same approach to problem solving as did Einstein. Though I may not be as intelligent as Al, nor do I have a circle of scientific friends or colleagues to bounce my thoughts off of, as did he, I have learned to enjoy solitude as much as Einstein did. The forced isolation of prison conditioned me to first begrudgingly endure, but ultimately appreciate, solitude. Much of Freud's thinking was also borne in "splendid isolation," supporting my belief that a regular dose of solitude, when mixed with a balanced life, is essential to intellectual progress.

Before we move on to the next chapter, I'll officially declare what I'm sure you already know: I have never donned a white coat and attached electrodes to someone's head. Nor have I personally worn an imaging cap, allowing someone else to observe my own brain in action. Quite frankly, as Freud once said, though the words describe me more accurately than him, "I am actually not at all a man of science." But I am a writer so I do hope that I have the ability to connect with you through words. And you and I are about to connect the dots that shine like constellations inside our three pound universe.

Let us enter the brain.

Chapter Fourteen
Moses and the Mind

Until the second half of the twentieth century, detectives were expected to solve criminal cases with very little help from science. That's probably why we still don't know for certain the true identity of Jack the Ripper. Back then, police looked at a victim's eyeballs to see if a photographic image of the killer was captured on the lens. Today, detectives use advanced scientific methods to help them solve cases: fingerprinting, blood spatter analysis, facial reconstruction, polygraph tests, toxicology tests, and DNA. In fact, you can almost trace the development of forensic science through TV cop shows. In the 1970s and 80s, a good cop show was filled with wild shoot-outs and car chases; not much, if any, science. Today, TV shows like *CSI*, *Bones*, *Law and Order*, and other cop dramas have become more cerebral, highlighting the use of forensic evidence to nail the culprits.

During this same time frame, the evolution of neuroscience has also come a long way. Let's briefly trace that evolution since neuroscience will help us pinpoint the command center for *Sleep AID*.

The brain looks like a head of cauliflower, though not as firm. When devoid of life, it is of less value than this vegetable—unless it's Einstein's brain, which was worth enough for someone to steal it, place it into two glass cookie jars, and hold onto it for forty-three years, sometimes driving around with it in his car, sometimes doling out tiny pieces of it to his close friends. This thief who'd performed Einstein's autopsy and made off with his brain claimed he'd done it in the name of science. But Einstein's mind could not be understood by examining the dead tissue it once dwelled in any more than we can understand the mind of Peking Man by examining his empty skull.[12]

---

[12] Within seven hours of Einstein's death, his autopsy was performed at Princeton Hospital in New Jersey. His brain was removed by pathologist Thomas Harvey who later made "caliper measurements," took "calibrated photographs," and cut up the cerebral hemispheres "into approximately 240 blocks." After the fact, it appears that Einstein's son, Hans Albert, was sort of wrangled into consenting to the donation of his dad's brain for science. Had he refused, I'm sure Harvey would have paid Einstein's other son, Eduard, a visit over at the asylum, maybe with a tray of baked brownies wrapped up in a consent form. Anyway, subsequent studies of Einstein's brain in comparison to thirty-five other male brains showed that "his brain weight did not differ" nor did "brain length, size of the corpus collosum, and measures of the frontal and temporal lobes." However, "in the parietal lobes, there were striking quantitative differences." This appeared to be the only exception and happens to be a region that helps with our sense of space. The study was inconclusive and somewhat speculatory as other physicists and mathematicians are also reported to have larger than normal parietal lobes but they have not come up with anything remotely comparable to $E=mc^2$. Drs. Marion Diamond and Arnold Scheibel also asked Harvey for some of Einstein's brain tissue. Rather generous with another man's brain, Harvey doled out a few slices and participated in their subsequent paper which concluded that Einstein's brain had more glial cells than other brains. However, no one is yet to make a connection between more glial cells and intelligence. As Arthur Schopenhauer has said, "A man can *do* what he wants, but not *want* what he wants," and that ultimately decides who each of us will be in life, a part of our minds which our brains do not yet reveal.

Until the latter part of the nineteenth century, we weren't certain that the mind and brain were sharing an apartment together. With the exception of a few ancient thinkers like Alcmaeon of Croton, most doctors and philosophers in the ancient world thought that the heart was the seat of our emotions. Hippocrates, who lived around the time of the Greek statesman Pericles, got it right when he wrote, "It ought to be generally known that the source of our pleasure, merriment, laughter, and amusement, as our grief, pain, anxiety, and tears, is none other than the brain. It is specially the organ which enables us to think, see, and hear…the seat of madness and delirium, of the fears and frights which assail us, often by night, but sometimes even by day."

Unable to establish credible evidence to support his conclusion, Hippocrates' words fell on deaf ears. So a few hundred years later, men were still scratching their heads not knowing what went on inside those itchy domes. Around Julius Caesar's time, Philo of Alexandria contemplated the same question Hippocrates had already answered, "In what part does the mind lie hid? Has it received any settled habitation…Some men have dedicated it to our head, as the principal citadel…Some again contend…that it is enshrined like a statue in the heart."

The Ancients may not have known for sure where the mind dwelled but they did recognize a definite distinction between mind and body. Plato repeatedly distinguished between the two in his writings; he also believed that one could be ruled by only part of the mind, an idea that long anticipated the genius of Freud.

This "mind-body problem" continued all the way up until the seventeenth century when philosopher-mathematician Rene Descartes wrote a book called *Dualism* in which he outlined the concept that the mind (res cogitans or thinking thing) was distinct from the body. Incidentally, Descartes' motivation to write *Dualism* stemmed directly from a dream. (Once again, a dream plays a part in the history of science and the destiny of humankind.)

Though Descartes wrote an interesting and popular book, it did not put the mind-body problem to rest. In the twentieth century, the problem was moved, though not solved, as the ongoing dilemma evolved into the mind-brain problem (as opposed to mind-body).

Today, some scientists believe in an updated mind-brain version of dualism while others lean toward materialism which postulates that the mind and brain are one and the same. Pioneering neuroscientist, Sir Charles Sherrington, wrote, "That our being should consist of two fundamental elements offers, I suppose, no greater inherent improbability than that it should rest on only one," while MIT cognitive scientist Marvin Minsky has stated to the contrary, "Minds are simply what brains do." I happen to be in agreement with the opinion of neurologist Wilder Penfield who wrote, "I reject the concept that one must be either a monist or a dualist because that suggests a closed mind." (Note that I have tried to distinguish between brain and mind in this very book; sometimes this was easy while other times difficult.)

Albert Einstein, for one, can never be accused of having a closed mind. He knew that the pursuit of scientific theory is a tricky but worthwhile endeavor as hard work is never for naught. He once said, "Every theory is killed sooner or later...But if the theory has good in it, that good is embodied and continued in the next theory."

Enter Franz Joseph Gall, a quack who swore that subtle contours in our skulls identified certain traits of our characters. Gall's pseudoscience was called phrenology and it caught on in Parisian salons where pseudo-intellectuals (which I happen to be) massaged each other's heads while talking crap.[13]

But Gall was on to something when, in 1810, he claimed that particular areas of the brain were in command of certain faculties. Borrowing from Einstein's quote above, this part of Gall's theory had some "good in it," and would be "embodied and continued in the next theory." The wheel of history continued to turn and the torch of

---

[13] Gall's life is strikingly similar to Freud's life. Both men completed their degrees in Vienna and practiced there as well, though Gall developed "cranioscopy" (later phrenology) around 1800 while Freud developed "psychoanalysis" around 1900. Both theories were received with abounding skepticism. The scientific community's hostility toward Freud only strengthened his resolve to stay in spite of his declaring, "I hate Vienna." He only left when the German military invaded in 1938. Gall, on the other hand, fled to Napoleonic France hoping his theory would be welcome in the revolutionary atmosphere which craved anything avant-garde. The rich and bored loved Gall though Napoleon and his Institute of France deemed his science invalid.

science was passed; around the same time Gall dropped dead, Paul Broca was born.

While Broca was still waiting for hair to sprout on his chest, a little dispute was simmering between scientists who believed in cerebral localization—their core ideas stemmed from Gall's phrenology—and scientists who were opposed to it.

Finally, Broca, all grown up and ready to rumble, stepped onto the world stage when he stumbled upon a man nicknamed "Tan-Tan" who, sadly, could only mutter the words, "Tan-Tan." Tan-Tan was a patient at the Bicetre Hospital in France where he, even more sadly, dropped dead a few days after Broca had visited him. Though Broca was eagerly waiting, saw and scalpel at the ready, to cut into Tan-Tan's brain, we can't accuse him of murder. Though if I were a French detective back then, I'd have questioned the timing of Broca's visit. We can certainly imagine how happy Broca was to see Tan-Tan go—in the name of science, of course. After opening up Tan-Tan's skull, Broca spotted a lesion in the frontal lobe of the left cerebral hemisphere; in my language, somewhere between the eyebrow and the temple where zits tend to accumulate in high school.

Eureka! Broca knew what this meant: the ability to articulate language is localized in this area of the brain. The area is forever named Tan-Tan's area. Yeah right! How about Broca's area. You didn't think the poor schlep who suffered was going to get any credit, did you? Honorable mention, that's it.

Anyway, the discovery of Broca's area led to an entire mapping of the brain, a quest to identify what area was responsible for what function.[14] Scientists pored over the brain's landscape with as much zeal as nineteenth century imperialists running off to stake claims in their Scramble for Africa. Though lines can be drawn to divide the map of a continent, imperialists would never capture the African mind. Likewise, though scientists divided the brain into numerous little areas, they are yet unable to capture the ever elusive human mind. (It's important to note that no part of the brain operates in isolation. The brain is an interconnected network and signals from other parts of the brain flow in and out of localized areas.)

Unable to get hold of the mind, scientists continued to examine what they could see and hold: brain matter. In 1887, Ramon Cajal discovered the neuron, and the real whammy he dropped on the scientific community was that neurons communicate with one another without touching. In 1906, the same year Cajal scooped up his Nobel, Charles Scott Sheridan published a paper concerning his landmark

---

[14] Long before Gall and Broca, the Ancients took a stab at the idea of localization. Galen (130CE-200CE) worked on wounded gladiators and noticed that certain head injuries affected particular bodily functions. Even before Galen, Hippocrates (460 BCE –370 BCE) made the same connection. And more recently, in relation to the first two men, Avicenna (980CE-1037CE) imagined the brain having different chambers for different functions.

In the seventeenth century, Thomas Willis dissected animal and human brains trying to trace the connection between regions and functions. His 1664 book, *Cerebri Anatome*, marks the first time the word "neurologia" (later neurology) was seen in print. Still, Broca's area was the first to be universally accepted as having a direct link between region and function.

discovery of synapses which are tiny chemical bridges used to transmit messages from one neuron to another. Thanks to the exhausting work of these and many other devoted scientists, we've made tremendous *head*way, though we're still no closer to cracking the mind-brain problem.

Today, scientists who wish to explore the brain no longer beg morticians and prison wardens for cadavers, or hover over hospital beds waiting for Tan-Tan's to take a dirt nap. We now have MRI machines (magnetic resonance imaging) which allow us to trace the connection between mental processes and neural activity[15].

There are about one hundred billion neurons in the brain and these neurons are constantly signaling each other, carrying on a conversation. By looking at an MRI monitor we can identify which specific area of the brain is active when we speak, hear, feel, love, hate, learn, move, recall certain people and places, even think about sex (let's not forget Freud); in short, whatever our brains are up to, we can spy on like a nosy neighbor, via MRI.

Since Freud has mentioned Moses, noted earlier in this book, I'll refer to an episode in Moses' life to draw an analogy for how an MRI works in relation to the mind. Whether you believe in the Bible or not, it's a pretty good story.

---

[15] Scanning the brain can include such methods as Nuclear Magnetic Resonance Imaging (NMR), Positron Emission Topography (PET), Near-Infrared Spectroscopy (NIRS), Electroencephalography (EEG), and Magnetoencephalography (MEG), though MRI is sufficient to explain the basis of how it all works.

In the Bible's book of Exodus, Moses asks God, "Let me see your Glory." God may have interpreted the question to mean, "Let me see you" because God answered, "You cannot see My face…I will place you in the cleft of the rock and screen you with My hand until I have passed by."

Moses took what he could get. He got a good night's sleep and early the next morning he ate a big bowl of manna and milk for breakfast then climbed Mount Sinai for the umpteenth time. (Incidentally, Moses took up mountain climbing at age eighty proving that age is just a number.) That day, God "passed before [Moses] face" and when Moses descended the mountain, "the skin on [Moses] face was radiating."

Now let's imagine the mind and the brain. God will be the mind (how apropos) and Moses will be the brain, which happens to be in the cleft of a rock, or the skull. When the mind passes along routes in the brain, the image monitor radiates, as did Moses' face, so we can trace the path of the mind after it has "passed."

No sooner have I written this analogy and I'm wondering if I've made this clear, or could this little story be misinterpreted as an infantile masturbation fantasy. "A hand," "a rock," "hiding in a cleft," which is a clear allusion to boobs. Ah, hell, I think I'm clear, let's move on.

Just as the Bible has pieced together an image of God that is still quite puzzling, neuroscientists have pieced together an image of the mind—which is still quite puzzling.

The moral of the story is that, as Moses was unable to see God, we may never be able to see the mind. But we can see where it has "passed" and that helps us to piece together what's happening upstairs, and will also enable us to locate the whereabouts of *Sleep AID*.

Chapter Fifteen
Surveillance

Most organized crime investigations begin
with photo and audio surveillance. When law
enforcement officers feel they have gathered
sufficient photo and audio evidence against a suspect
or suspects, they hand over that evidence to a
prosecutor who sifts through it and weighs the
chances of winning a conviction at trial. Should the
prosecutor decide to move forward with an
indictment, the evidence is introduced at trial. It's
important to note that photo and audio evidence,
when used against co-conspirators, seldom contains
explicit confessions though such evidence is still
presented to a jury in the hope of gaining a
conviction.

If the courts needed a smoking gun to
convince a jury, hardly anyone would ever be
convicted of a crime. The prosecution therefore
builds a convincing case and allows the jury to
decide from there. In our case against Time, I plan to
do the same. Allow me to present the prosecution's
photo evidence. For our first witness I'll call to the
stand Dr. Dean Radin.

Dr. Radin graduated magna cum laude from
the University of Massachusetts, Amherst, and has
held appointments at Princeton University and the
University of Edinburgh. Over the years, this
humble looking genius has conducted some very
interesting experiments that offer surprising insights
into human consciousness.

In one particular experiment that's been repeated several times with the same results, Radin placed volunteers in front of a computer screen. Electrodes were attached to the fingers of the subjects' left hands to monitor heart rate and electrodermal activity (or electrical conductance of the skin) while their right hands were placed on a computer mouse. When the subjects clicked the mouse, the screen went blank for several seconds before the computer displayed an image at random from a preprogrammed pool of over one hundred images. Some of the images were scenes of serenity while other images were violent, shocking, or erotic. The experiments were double-blind, meaning that even the experimenter was unaware of what image would appear next.

Whenever the subjects clicked the mouse, their electrodermal activity heightened, a natural reaction as they anticipated the unknown image. But here's the kicker: the subjects' skin would react more than usual if the image about to pop up on the screen was one from the not-so-nice pool of images.

Nobel Prize winning chemist Kary Mullis was interested enough in Radin's findings to sit down as a subject. "I could see about three seconds into the future," said Mullis. "There's something funny about time...because you shouldn't be able to do that."

Another Nobel winner, Brian Josephson, commented on Radin's experiments, saying, "What seems to be happening is that information is coming from the future."

Apparently, some internal mechanism inside the brain is able to predict when the more shocking images will appear. And the predictions aren't luck or some form of card-counting mathematics; the odds of success in some of the experiments was 125,000 to 1, like falling into a haystack and getting poked in the ass by the needle.

Having introduced my photo evidence, let's move on to the audio evidence.

I'll begin with physicists Edwin C. May and James Spottiswoode who organized an experiment similar to the one conducted by Dr. Radin. I should quickly note that "physicist" is a pretty lofty title and the same one worn by Albert Einstein; I think Al would be proud of these kindred spirits venturing into the unknown as he had done.

May and Spottiswoode measured the electrodermal activity in more than one hundred subjects but this time the subjects were being exposed to loud noises as opposed to disturbing images. Headphones were placed on the subjects' ears and they were not told when the arrival of each sound would occur. Nor were the subjects able to decipher any predictable pattern. And the results: the subjects reacted "in advance significantly more before future audio stimuli than before future silent control stimuli."

In an article published in 2012 titled, "Predictive Physiological Anticipation Preceding Seemingly Unpredictable Stimuli," a team led by neuroscientist Julia Mossbridge wrote, "More than forty experiments published over the past 32 years examine the claim that human physiology predicts future important or arousing events, even though we do not currently understand how such a thing could be accomplished." Mossbridge's team also concluded, "There seems to be a small, predictive anticipatory physiological shift in the seconds preceding apparently unpredictable stimuli."

So what does this mean? Why would the human brain be programmed to detect noise before it occurs in real time?

The World Health Organization (WHO) monitors noise pollution amongst other health hazards. In a report titled, "Noise Effects and Morbidity," the organization detailed the hazardous effects noise can have on us while we're asleep.

The report reads that "Sleep is an essential condition for humans and can be severely disturbed by noise…noise induced sleep disturbances are associated for adults with significantly elevated risks for the vast majority of diseases…With children, noise induced sleep disturbances are statistically associated with a highly elevated risk of medical treatments due to bronchitis as well as with elevated risks for respiratory symptoms and for 'trend depression.'"

The report concluded that "Sleep can be severely disturbed by noise. Acute sleep disturbances effect performance and in the long run health. For adults, significantly elevated relative risks in the cardiovascular system, the respiratory system, and the musculoskeletal system as well as depression exists with noise induced sleep disturbances."

So noise can aggravate sleep, even to the point of killing us. And we might be better prepared if we knew when those noises are coming. Herein lies the primary purpose of *Sleep AID*, a primordial design hardwired into the brain to disguise distractions that might otherwise wake us and disrupt our sleep patterns. To achieve this, a region of the brain must be able to identify the external stimuli before it arrives in the present moment. The ultimate goal, like other real time incorporation dreams, such as the ringing telephone that also rings in our sleep, is to keep us asleep and prevent unnecessary exhaustion that would certainly, and negatively, affect our waking lives as well.

Here's how it happens: When the external stimuli occurs, like the sound of an automobile collision on my street corner, the noise from the crash is seamlessly incorporated into the dream narrative. At best, sleep is preserved as is homeostasis. Even if the noise rouses us from sleep, as did the crashes on my corner, the impact is lessened as it is received by the duped part of our brains as the stuff of harmless dreams. And being awakened by a dream is much easier to deal with for the mind and body than a sudden external intrusion. Thus, an otherwise startling event is instead slowly and harmlessly absorbed with each microsecond of awareness as we awaken.

Allow me to point out that heightened electrodermal activity, like that exhibited by Radin, and May and Spottiswoode's experiments, is also a standard reaction we undergo when our fight or flight response is activated. Dr. Radin also tells us that, during his photo experiments, "pupillary dilation and spontaneous blinking were found to increase more before emotional versus calm photos." And I'll point out that dilation of the pupils is yet another fight or flight response.

Thus, certain bodily reactions that are stimulated in these experiments also shift into high gear when our fight or flight response is activated. We can therefore deduce that the region of the brain that reacts to future stimuli is the same region that initiates our fight or flight response. Where is this region?

Being that I've already used investigative techniques found in organized crime cases, I'll do the same in the next chapter, this time to locate the whereabouts of *Sleep AID*.

Chapter Sixteen
The Hang-Out

Ordinarily, law enforcement will conduct surveillance on any hang-out known to be frequented by members of a criminal organization. At trial, photos of various characters who frequent the hang-out are displayed on a large board for the jury to see. The justifiable conclusion is that whoever dwells together smells together. Thus, the hang-out becomes a major component in the prosecutor's plight to prove that the defendants have been, at the very least, rather chummy; at worst, acting in concert with regard to a criminal conspiracy. I'll now inform you where the *Sleep AID* organization has been hanging out.

The lower part of our brain is called the brainstem. Areas of the brainstem are concerned with alertness and also survival which includes heart rate, breathing, and blood pressure. The brainstem is also hell-bent on keeping the body adapted to the changes of our outside environment. The rest of our brain can be wandering off in la-la land while survival remains the brainstem's primary function. Located within the brainstem is the reticular formation which is a number of nerve pathways that carry sensory messages to our cortex, which is the big upper part of our brain. The reticular formation and its various connecting networks form what is called the Reticular Activating System (RAS).

To illustrate how the RAS works, I'll use an example from World War II. During an early period of the war referred to as the Battle of Britain, Britain's Royal Air Force, or RAF, would receive information when enemy German Luftwaffe planes were crossing the Channel and respond by sounding alarms all over London, while at the same time, RAF pilots would take to the sky to confront the oncoming threat.

The RAS to the human body is very similar to what the RAF was to Britain during the war. When a potentially dangerous threat to our person arises, the RAS sounds an alarm and tells the rest of the brain and body to get ready to meet the oncoming threat. So the brain's RAS is like Britain's RAF, protecting us from danger—but only while we're awake.

While we're asleep, the sensitivity of the reticular formation is dialed down. Sadly, a lot of cruel experiments have been done on cats, resulting in our understanding of the reticular formation. I'm a cat lover and I find them to be just like little people; unfortunately for cats, some researchers have drawn the same conclusion and have therefore found their brains ideal for experiments.

If the reticular formation in a cat is destroyed, nothing can wake it. No external stimuli, not even a pinch, can rouse it from sleep. In human terms, we can't have that or we'd be in trouble if the house went on fire. Nor can we be bothered for every false alarm or we'd never get any sleep. Thus a balancing act must take place. To start with, when we're asleep, the reticular formation is dialed down by the boss who sits at the top of the reticular formation. And the boss is the hypothalamus.

Who does the hypothalamus think it is that it can just tell the most vital part of our brain, in terms of defense and survival, to dial down? The hypothalamus rules over "a vast domain." In size it has been compared to an olive, a chestnut, and a sugar cube; since none of these do it for me I'm going to compare it to a Hershey's Kiss. Despite its tiny size, it is "the grand master of virtually all of the body's involuntary or autonomic functions." (What can be worse than a tiny brain part with a Napoleon complex?)

To get a clear understanding of how smart the hypothalamus is, think about this: In 1620, the earliest record of a thermostat appeared in England. The hypothalamus has been controlling the body's thermostat since our appearance on Earth, responding to environmental temperatures in order to meticulously regulate our body temperatures. In 1628, William Harvey finally convinced the world that the heart is responsible for circulating blood throughout the body. The hypothalamus has been regulating our heartbeats and circulation forever. Our best inventions only mimic what the brain has been doing since the dawn of humankind; the computer is an obvious modern example as is artificial intelligence. So the hypothalamus is pulling an awful lot of strings but let's stick to those that are relevant to our investigation.

To start with, the suprachiasmatic nucleus (SCN) is found in the hypothalamus. And the SCN is the location of our body clock, better known as our circadian clock. The SCN tells us when to go to sleep and when to awaken.

Now recall at the end of the last chapter when I pointed out that precognitive experiments are shown to provoke certain bodily reactions that are also aroused during our fight or flight response. Note that the command center for these fight or flight reactions is also found in the hypothalamus. When our fight or flight response is activated, here are the things this little Hershey's Kiss-sized command center will do to protect us in the flash of a second: "An increase in neurotransmitters enhances alertness. Blood vessels to muscles dilate; those in areas with less urgent needs constrict. Heart rate and blood pressure increase to rush blood to active areas. The liver converts starches to glucose. Fat breaks down into fatty acids, another fuel. The pupils widen to let in more light and improve peripheral vision. Sweat production increases, making the body difficult to grab, and body hair rises, a holdover function to make the body look larger. Bronchioles dilate to take in more oxygen. The adrenal medulla speed up body metabolism, and the blood's clotting powers increase. Meanwhile, unnecessary functions such as digestion are suppressed."

A brilliant little thing this hypothalamus is, orchestrating all that while we're pooping in our pants (quite literally since we may actually do this in order to unload excess waste and make flight easier). Now tell me, would the hypothalamus, which controls this intricate web of bodily reactions designed for our survival, simply put us to sleep each night and leave us completely vulnerable with no means of security? Why go through all that by day only to doze off at night when we can get mauled and eaten? We'll get to that shortly.

So far, I've pointed out that our sleep clock and fight or flight mechanism are both found in the hypothalamus. And here's another connection between sleep and fight or flight: a neurotransmitter called norepinephrine works in the sympathetic nervous system, also controlled by the hypothalamus. Norepinephrine generates our fight or flight responses. Norepinephrine is also one of the neurotransmitters known to promote wakefulness; it acts to excite the cortex and keep us awake during the wake cycle of our days. But the hypothalamus tells norepinephrine to decrease at the onset of sleep while it simultaneously shuts down pathways which maintain wakefulness so all excitatory neurotransmitters, like norepinephrine, can't get through. When the hypothalamus receives information from its own circadian clock to shut us down for sleep, it tells norepinephrine to take a walk. Beat it. Scram. Don't call me, I'll call you! From here on out, throughout the long night, the hypothalamus must decide when to call on norepinephrine and wake us for danger, and when to let us remain asleep which is just as important for survival as verified by reports from the World Health Organization.

The first member of the *Sleep AID* organization has been identified and my investigation is moving along well but I've not yet rounded up all the culprits. While keeping a close eye on the hypothalamus, I noticed a close associate called the thalamus. The Mafia uses the terms "boss" and "underboss" to describe the number one and number two men in a mafia family. Hypo means "under" in Latin, and the term is used because the hypothalamus sits "under" another small region of the brain called the thalamus, thus the name hypothalamus. But don't let the names fool you. Like a smart mafia don who puts up a front man to look like the boss, the hypothalamus may have "under" in its name, but it's really the boss.

So who is the thalamus? Through our sensory receptors we receive a constant flow of information from our environment. The sensory messages are routed through the thalamus, finally arriving at the cortex where we process the signals. Watch a sunset, ah how pretty; starts in the eyes, ends in the cortex. Stub your toe, ooh, that hurts; starts in the foot, ends in the cortex. But these sensory messages that pass along routes in the body to get to the cortex must first pass through a relay station that sits at the top of the hypothalamus, and that relay station is the thalamus. And whenever we fall asleep at night, the thalamus becomes the gatekeeper, "Who goes there?" for the ascending information traveling to the cortex.

More specifically, it is the reticular nucleus of the thalamus that allows activity to flow or closes the gates.[16] So the thalamus, or gatekeeper, takes its orders from the boss, or hypothalamus.

---

[16] To emphasize the importance of this thalamic gatekeeper, there exists an extremely rare disease called Fatal Familial Insomnia which attacks the thalamus and in doing so, disarms the gatekeeper. After the onset of this disease, sleep becomes nearly or totally impossible and death awaits. It is a tragic disease that reinforces the importance of sleep as a life and death matter and also lends credence to the theory of *Sleep AID* as a vital necessity for survival.

Who else has been caught hanging around with this little crew of brainiacs? A mafia crew usually has what they call a button man. That's the guy who takes orders; you push his button when you need something done. I've known these guys, they're very emotional and seem to have a temper they can switch on like a faucet. A boss can point to a night club and say, "Wreck it!" and a good button man will run inside and do just that, no questions asked. He doesn't think much and his job is to instill fear. So take note of the button man's attributes: highly emotional and bent on instilling fear. Okay, now let's meet our brain's button man, the amygdala. The amygdala interacts with the hypothalamus (the boss) and the thalamus (the underboss).

The Incredible Hulk, when still mild-mannered David Banner, is known to warn people who are pushing his buttons with the words, "You won't like me when I'm angry." Well, that's the amygdala, our button man. It is literally full of emotions and even generates the emotions in our dreams. That's right, "the amygdala, an almond-shaped gland responsible for emotion, goes ballistic during dreams."

So the amygdala, which acts on emotions, cannot be a good leader since we can't have a raging monster or a cry baby controlling the human brain and body. (Well, not all the time.) Since the amygdala "operates unconsciously, and is thus liable to produce errors" it therefore transmits distress signals to the hypothalamus and relies on the cool and collected hypothalamus to mediate its fear reactions. This is how it happens: "A frightening sight or sound registers in the amygdala *before we are even conscious of it*…the amygdala sends messages to the hypothalamus, which triggers changes that ready the body for flight, fight, or appeasement."

Here's a personal example of how fast the amygdala reacts to our external environment. During my incarceration, I had lived in numerous prisons and encountered thousands of convicts. Back then I relied on what I believed were my instincts to tell me who I should be wary of. It might have been a convict's face or a mannerism that revealed to me some hidden evil and told me, "Watch out for this guy." But if I was asked to explain exactly what clues were warning me of potential danger, in many cases, I honestly couldn't tell you. I'd eventually learn that there's an explanation for that feeling I would have.

The amygdala, which is the "threat center" of the brain, "registers the emotional faces of others, and produces a reaction before we even know we have seen them." It even responds to images that are flashed before our eyes too quickly for us to recognize them. One study from Uppsala University in Sweden has shown that "unconscious presentation of negative facial stimuli evokes increased neural activity in the human amygdala." And another study by a joint team from Switzerland, France, and the United States shows "an involvement of the amygdala in response to untrustworthy faces." If untrustworthy faces can trigger the amygdala, needless to say, my amygdala must have been overworked in prison.

In addition to subliminal recognition, "the human amygdala plays a pivotal role in triggering a state of fear." In a brilliant series of experiments, a woman with focal bilateral amygdala lesions, or a damaged amygdala, was placed in various situations in which a state of fear should have been triggered within her. For example, she was terrified of snakes and spiders yet when brought to a pet store and led over to a tank with snakes, she showed absolutely no fear, even holding the snakes. She even tried to pick up a tarantula though she was prudently stopped by the scientists. (Broca would have dropped it down Tan-Tan's shirt.)

The scientists concluded their report by saying, "Her behavior, time and again, leads her back to the very situations she should be avoiding, highlighting the indispensable role that the amygdala plays in promoting survival by compelling the organism away from danger. Indeed, it appears that without the amygdala, the evolutionary value of fear is lost."

So we've established that our amygdala is responsible for fear and therefore involved in fight or flight. But when we're asleep, the amygdala is busy generating the emotional themes of our dreams. So once again we have a localized area of the brain that is concerned with threats and fight or flight by day, and a major participant in our dreamwork by night. It is too coincidental for me to believe that evolution has accidentally placed the main threat areas of the brain in the same exact places that participate in our dreams if not for the simple and economic reason that these areas are best equipped to balance the two polar opposite states with utmost facility. And one of the brilliant ways in which they do so is through *Sleep AID*, designed to preserve sleep and homeostasis, and in turn health, by shielding us from startling noises and therefore avoiding our fight or flight responses when such reactions are unwarranted. But in order to decide if we should be shielded from noises or awakened for danger, the amygdala must have a keen eye toward the future. And we've established through waking experiments that it does indeed possess this foresight.

To support my claim that the amygdala lies at the center of the *Sleep AID* process, I'll quote from a few of the many research papers that allow us to clearly link the amygdala to photo experiments cited earlier in this book. One report from *The Journal of Neuroscience* states that "evidence for the role of the amygdala in the expression of skin conductance responses (SCR's) comes from both functional imaging studies and lesion studies." Another study using an MRI shows that "the amygdala was activated by the processing of highly interesting and unusual pictures even when they were emotionally neutral."

As for audio experiments, we again find the amygdala's fingerprints at the scene. A London experiment in which subjects listened to their own names during sleep concluded that "the amygdala may play a role in mediating the response to auditory stimuli with affective significance is not surprising...amygdala responses to behaviorally relevant stimuli can occur without awareness."

Given the studies above, I can therefore deduce that this same amygdala that "goes ballistic during dreams" and "may play a role in mediating the response to auditory stimuli" is the area equipped to recognize, for example, the car accidents on my corner before they occurred. Already actively engaged in the dreamwork and well prepared to move fast, the amygdala, sensing an impending auditory distraction, spins a dream to meet its arrival. If a true threat presents itself—not just a noise—it appears that the ever informed hypothalamus will step in and mediate the body's response.

While we're awake, we are constantly under a barrage of distractions and a sensory filter decides what gets through to our consciousness, which amounts to our reality. How else can we attend a loud party or a baseball game without being overwhelmed by sensory anarchy? While asleep, this same sensory filter must make precise distinctions for safety reasons; what presents a threat or the need for waking—like a baby crying—and what does not.

When no real threat is posed, the chief concern is to maintain sleep. To do so, the level and suddenness of distractions must be measured and incorporated into our dreams if necessary. But some degree of foresight is necessary to achieve success since loud, sudden distractions would rudely rouse us before the dreaming brain has an opportunity to incorporate them.[17]

---

[17] Ernst Heinrich Weber (1795-1878) has given us Weber's law, later expanded upon by the work of Gustav Theodor Fechner (1801-1887). Weber's law precisely measures the slightest sensitivity between varying degrees of stimuli, and also determines the absolute threshold needed for the senses to detect stimuli. The dreaming mind must also distinguish

The amygdala, sensing an impending distraction, commands the dreaming society of the mind—which happens to have a main office within its own locale—to spin a dream and meet the stimuli's arrival. When the stimuli arrives, it is seamlessly incorporated into the dream narrative. At best, sleep is preserved as is homeostasis. At worst, the blow is lessened as it is received by the duped part of our brains as the stuff of harmless dreams.[18]

---

between varying degrees of external stimuli in order to decide what gets seamlessly incorporated in real time, like a ringing telephone, and what will be loud enough to require a back story to meet the noise's arrival in real time. Extreme personalities represent the danger of not being able to differentiate between degrees. For example, a con I'll call D.J. thought that everyone was out to get him and was regularly launching a preemptive attack on other cons, sometimes hurting them, sometimes getting hurt himself; in extreme cases, nearly killed. On the other hand, a con I'll call J.D. believed himself to be untouchable and was severely sliced across the face with a razor. Most cons who survive their prison experience unscathed have the inherent ability to measure what exactly presents a threat, and decide what threats require action; moreover, what degree of action. The dreaming mind must also possess the ability to differentiate between distractions; what is too trivial to warrant a distraction, what must be incorporated, what requires back story, and when sleep should be disrupted. Thus, the dreaming mind must have a Weber's law in place to differentiate between degrees of distractions.

[18] There are levels of consciousness within the brain that communicate but are distinct. Split brain patients provide an excellent example of at least two independent streams of consciousness existing in each hemisphere of the brain. To emphasize the multiple minds within the dreaming brain, cognitive psychologist John Antrobus says, "What always fascinated me about dreams was how your brain created something that was surprising to itself." Neurobiologist Michel Jouvet described dreaming as "a third state of the brain, which

If the stimuli rouses us from sleep, we are being awakened by a dream, much easier to deal with than a sudden external intrusion, an event that is now slowly and harmlessly absorbed with each microsecond of awareness. If a true threat presents itself—not just a noise—it appears that the hypothalamus, which may also be possessed of foresight, will step in and mediate the body's response.

Dear reader and member of this jury, I have called on expert witnesses from the fields of physics, neuroscience, and psychology. I've presented my photo and audio evidence. And I've located the main hang-out where the *Sleep AID* organization is controlling its empire. I now ask you to weigh this evidence while I prepare my closing arguments.

---

was as different from sleep as sleep is from wakefulness." And finally our man Freud went even further than Jouvet when he said, "We must be prepared, it would appear, to assume the existence not only of a second consciousness in us, but of a third and fourth also, perhaps of an infinite series of states of consciousness, each and all unknown to us and to one another." Thus the notion that one level of consciousness will mislead another to preserve health and safety is not beyond reason.

Chapter Seventeen
The Summation

Like any good prosecutor, I've presented my evidence, called on expert witnesses, and now I arrive at the part of this trial in which I'll make my closing arguments, or summation. If I've presented strong evidence and my witnesses were deemed credible, then my final task should be relatively easy.

I had first worked out the theory of *Sleep AID* in a prison cell. Let us return there for a moment where I'm talking with a fellow convict who had stopped by to ask me some questions about the book I was reading. Our conversation went from one subject to another until I somehow found myself explaining to him the structure of government in the United States. His questions were basic and the final one, which I'll presently relate to you, should indicate the intelligence level of at least one man who was expected to understand the complex court proceedings that restricted his life to a human dog kennel for forty years. I assure you he understood as little about the minds and mechanisms that placed him in this kennel than Laika the dogmonaut did of the minds and mechanisms that thrust her into space and back.

After I had explained to him how the three branches of government work in the United States, he asked me if all three branches had to take part in a decision to nuke another country. In the event of an emergency, I told him, the decision resides in the executive branch, or with the president. He nodded his head then asked, "What do we do when the president is sleeping?" I laughed at his naiveté, but affectionately, not maliciously.

We have a system in place, I explained, to secure the country from external threats 24/7. The president can be awakened if need be, while situations that don't qualify as a severe and immediate threat can wait till morning. He looked relieved, as if he again felt safe from a nuclear attack.

Over the years I've recalled this conversation to emphasize the need for our courts to assess the intelligence levels of adults before sentencing them to outrageous terms of imprisonment. Although we don't typically try a twelve-year-old as an adult, a man with a twelve-year-old mentality presents us with no problem. I'll now use this conversation as a perfect illustration for *Sleep AID*; a system must be in place to balance our need for sleep against our need to awaken and confront danger.

As a prisoner, I experienced isolation (in solitary confinement), sleep deprivation (while in transit), sensory deprivation (when isolated), and prolonged exposure to loud environments (when in the general population), all of which proved conducive to understanding my theory. When ultimately deciding to write this book, I asked myself two major questions before I began: Can I overlook my vivid experiences and explain them away as nonsense? Can I overlook the series of reinforcements that stemmed from my thorough inquiry? In the end, I felt to do so would be a larger offense to humanity than any crime I'd ever committed. And so began this daunting task.

Throughout this trial I called on expert witnesses such as Albert Einstein who established that Time is an illusion. I called on Alfred Maury who testified about his thousands of experiments with regard to incorporation of stimuli and recorded for us his most enlightening guillotine dream. I also called on contemporary dream researchers like William Dement whose tireless experiments have established, amongst countless other things, that dreams are dreamt in real time. And I called on Sigmund Freud who at first appeared as a witness for the defense, arguing against precognitive experiences, but with diligent research into his background and his prolific writings, Freud has presented us with a motive for his denial which, in turn, cast reasonable doubt upon his original testimony.

I moved on and explained a brief history of neuroscience which now allows us to monitor activity in the brain so we can trace what's happening and where. I then introduced photo and audio evidence that proved beyond any reasonable doubt that an area of our brain can respond to sights and sounds before they occur. We can therefore deduce that an impending incident of negative value, like Maury's bed breaking or cars colliding on my corner, can be sensed before the incidents happen in real time. I also pinpointed where this sort of mental radar appears to be located inside the brain; localized areas that are heavily involved in sleep and dreams as well as fight or flight, both crucial elements for survival.

Use of the term mental radar calls to mind an analogy I can use to demonstrate *Sleep AID*. During the surveillance phase of this trial, I compared the RAS (reticular activating system) to the RAF (Royal Air Force). During the Battle of Britain, the RAF deprived the German Luftwaffe the element of surprise by setting up a chain of radar stations that ran up and down the southeast coast of England, allowing pilots to get airborne and face German attackers with enough time to save the nation. Without radar, British planes could have been attacked on the ground and destroyed without a fight.

Radar has come a long way since World War II, but even then it was not so basic as to mistake a seagull or a kite for a Messerschmitt fighter plane. Radar is meticulously set so that birds and kites don't sound an alarm but airplanes do. In this manner, RAF pilots did not lose much needed sleep by responding to every false threat that blipped on the radar screen. And keeping the pilots fresh for combat meant the survival of Britain.

Humankind must also survive, and according to Freud survival is our greatest instinct, even stronger than sex (which of course is the means by which our species survives). To survive when the lights go out and we're fast asleep, the human brain is equipped with radar. It is no harder for me to believe that radar can be installed on a steel tower than it is for me to believe it is installed in our own brains. Surely the same brain that's intelligent enough to invent radar would have the best version of it available in its own home. (Recall in Chapter Sixteen how the brain often invents what it has long been doing internally. The brain invented the thermostat; it has its own thermostat. The brain invented the computer; it is a computer. Why should we be incredulous that it would have radar as it has invented that, too?)

In prison, you learn to sleep with one eye open. Literally, it's not a true statement, but dolphins do just that. In 1964, neuroscientist John Lilly observed that dolphins slept with one eye open and concluded that evolution has safeguarded their survival by putting only half of their brains to sleep at a time, as reflected by one closed eye. Why would we humans, who sit at the very top of the animal kingdom, be left vulnerable with both eyes shut?

We have a number of internal mechanisms which vigilantly guard our safety by day. Do you think they simply shut down each night and roll the dice with our survival for a total of one third of our lives, or 50,000 hours? Why work so hard to protect us only part of the time? Would you invest in a home security system that only protects your house during the day and leaves you and your family completely unprotected at night, when you really need it? Would you deposit your hard earned money in a bank vault that's locked during the day but left open all night long, with no security cameras? If you believe we're built to drift off to sleep without a secondary, highly sensitive, defense system in place, you're dreaming!

Ladies and gentlemen of the jury, I rest my case.

Epilogue

Recall the introduction to this book when I wrote about that peculiar moment in a London hotel room when I had noticed that both of my wristwatches had stopped ticking at or around the same time. The larger subject of Time had come to mind while by chance I was reading books about Einstein and Newton, and had visited Freud's home earlier that same day. So where is Newton in all of this mind, Time, and Space stuff? Not far.

Newtonian physics posits that clocks may tick to their own tune but a universal clock dictates the absolute pace of the universe. Einstein spotted Newton's incomplete theory of universal Time and in turn gave us his theories of relativity.

Ever since Einstein's theories of relativity were proven, many physicists agree that "the future exists as much as the past does; it is just in a place that we have not yet visited." Kurt Gödel, a dear friend of Einstein, and a man Freeman Dyson said was "the only one of our colleagues who walked and talked on equal terms with Einstein," was so sure that past, present, and future coexisted on some level that he "proved, from the equations of relativity, that time travel was not a philosopher's fantasy but a scientific possibility."

Today, physicists can talk about time travel without being confined to a strait jacket. But all of their "thought experiments"—which is all they are at this stage—are limited to the imagination. And even if time travel were possible, the realization of such a wild idea is not presently on our horizon. But the human brain is close at hand as it sits atop our shoulders. To explore it we don't need to build a spaceship or jazz up a DeLorean; we just need to dream, literally and figuratively.

When Einstein published his theories of relativity there was no way of proving the theories correct. But Einstein was confident, with the passing of time, others would do so for him. He once wrote in a letter to his pal, Marcel Grossmann, "I have got a few wonderful ideas in my head that have to be worked out in due course…perhaps the researches of others directed to different goals will ultimately prove the theory."

This hope turned into a plea when in 1911 Einstein published a paper titled, *The Influence of Gravity on the Propagation of Light*. In this paper, Einstein wrote, "It would be extremely desirable if astronomers would look into the problem presented here, even though the consideration developed above may appear insufficiently founded or even bizarre."

In 1919, years after Einstein published his papers on relativity, the constellations were lining up to prove him correct, here on Earth and in the heavens. In the heavens, a solar eclipse was about to take place, the perfect scenario to test Einstein's general theory of relativity. Here on Earth, the Royal Astronomical Society of London made arrangements to dispatch two teams to two potential observation posts where they could photograph the eclipse.

Willing, if need be, to dethrone their beloved Newton, the Brits sent one team to Brazil and the other to an island off the west coast of Africa. Sir Arthur Eddington led the African expedition and arrived on the island of Principe where he set up his photographic equipment. The eclipse only lasted a few minutes but long enough for Eddington and his team to snap sixteen photos. Eddington returned to England and analyzed his photographs with the help of other scientists, and on November 6, 1919, the Royal Astronomical Society officially announced the results that changed history. Einstein was correct!

When Einstein received news that his general theory of relativity had been validated, he hung up the telephone and calmly said to the woman next to him, "I knew the theory was correct." Well, excuse me! Guess he thought he was some kind of Einstein.

I'll sum up my own hopes for *Sleep AID* by combining Einstein's two quotes just mentioned above: "Even though the consideration developed above may appear insufficiently founded or even bizarre…perhaps the researches of others directed to different goals will ultimately prove the theory."

I haven't the slightest doubt that science will soon confirm in multiple experiments that *Sleep AID* is real, and I've striven over the course of this book to begin a conversation and lay the groundwork for a valid theory "since no experiment can be conceived without some sort of theory." I'm sure dream researchers will come up with plenty of ways to test the theory. As for the world of physics, a good place to start searching for evidence may be in the field of quantum mechanics.

A contemporary of Einstein and fellow physicist by the name of Max Planck came up with the basis for quantum theory, later quantum mechanics. (Planck figured out that Mother Nature packages energy in tiny units called quanta.) Without getting too deep into this puzzling field of science, suffice it to say that quantum mechanics draws a couple of weird conclusions in relation to consciousness. First, observing an object in a particular place may cause it to be there. (If there is a hidden variable at work it is yet undiscovered.) Second, an object can influence the behavior of another object "even if they are on opposite sides of the universe...notwithstanding the many trillions of miles of space between them, it's as if they are right on top of each other." Einstein found quantum mechanics extremely hard to accept and referred to the mysterious influences behind the second conclusion as "spooky actions at a distance."

Spooky, mysterious, or whatever, it is a fact that when dealing with quantum mechanics, physics encounters consciousness at every turn. Nobel laureate Eugene Wigner stated, "It is not possible to formulate the laws of quantum mechanics in a fully consistent way without reference to the consciousness."

When the public first read H.G. Wells' *Time Machine*, I'm not sure how many readers could have imagined that a German Jewish physicist, who looked like he'd combed his hair with a hand grenade, would come along and force us to imagine the validity of at least the premise for Wells' fantasy novel. As a tribute to Wells, who got us all thinking, I'll sum up this very book with two quotes from Wells' *Time Machine*.

On the opening page, the Time Traveler says, "I do not mean to ask you to accept anything without reasonable ground." I now ask the same of you for *Sleep AID*.

On the closing page of *Time Machine*, Wells writes, "It remains for us to live as though it were not so…to me the future is still black and blank—is a vast ignorance, lit at a few random places." I agree, but let's explore those random places and see where it leads us.

I bid you sweet dreams, and may Time be generous with the days of your life.

Acknowledgements

I copyrighted the first draft of this book in January 2014 but didn't know what to do with it since I'm not a member of the scientific community and soon learned that this group is more tight-knit than the Mafia. However, I was fortunate to be invited as a guest speaker for the 2014 CEO Global Leaders Forum held in New York City. While at the event, I attended a number of sessions, one of which was presented by Dr. Mary Case, titled, "Seeing Thinking: The Human Brain *In Vivo*." After the session, I struck up a conversation with Dr. Case and the following week she was kind enough to take time out of her busy schedule to read my manuscript. I thank her for that.

Another session I attended at this event was titled, "A Constructive Conversation About Climate Change," presented by MIT atmospheric physicist Richard Lindzen. Dr. Lindzen and I attended lunch together where we conversed about European history. I also told Dr. Lindzen about my latest manuscript. Following the event, Dr. Lindzen put me in contact with his son, a neuroscientist named Dr. Eric Lindzen, who read my manuscript and provided some helpful comments. I thank Drs. Lindzen and Lindzen for their unique kindness.

I'd like to thank Dr. Philip M. Tierno Jr., a rare genius who is able to see things in our tiny world of microbiology as clearly as I see the page I'm writing on.

Dr. Tierno is also a gifted writer and I thank him for reading my manuscript. I highly recommend his books if interested in the fascinating microworld around us, and within us.

Gabriella, my better half, is always patiently waiting for me to complete my final edit so she can hop in and point out anything I've overlooked. Though this was a subject she knew very little about, her comments in the way of clarity were spot-on.

I thank Dr. Dean Radin and IONS President Dr. Cassandra Vieten, who invited me to speak about my theory at the IONS 16th International Conference.

Thanks to Bruce and Madeline Ramer, David Black, Harry Stein, Bill Yosses, Edward Kanaley, John Farrar, Ryan Kerrison, Tilman Remme, Larry Steckman, Eric Kreuter, my father and Betty, my sister Lisa and Ralph, Don and Debbie, Denise and John, Aunt Claudette and Uncle Anthony.

I'd like to acknowledge that the book titled, *The Three Pound Universe,* was written by Judith Hooper and Dick Teresi. Since its publication in 1986, the title has become an oft-quoted phrase, and the title of my own book stems from this phrase.

Lastly, I thank the many scientists who tirelessly labor away without recognition. Their exhaustive research is etched deep into the pages of history while their names are sadly left out of the acknowledgements. Without these men and women, we'd all be lost.

Notes

vii The distinction between: From Einstein's letter of condolence to the Besso family, March 21, 1955, in the Einstein Archive 7-245, as quoted in Walter Isaacson, *Einstein: His Life and Universe* (New York: Simon & Schuster, 2007), p. 540.

vii The processes of: From "The Unconscious," trans. Cecil M. Baines, 1915, in Sigmund Freud, *Sigmund Freud: Collected Papers*, Authorized Translation Under the Supervision of Joan Riviere (New York: Basic Books, 1959), 4:119.

ix the life of the individual: From "Is There a Jewish Point of View?" in Albert Einstein, *Ideas and Opinions: Based on Mein Weltbild*, ed. Carl Seelig and Other Sources, new trans. and rev. Sonja Bargmann (New York: Crown, 1954), p. 186.

xii lazy dog: Banesh Hoffmann, with the collaboration of Helen Dukas, *Albert Einstein: Creator and Rebel* (New York: Viking, 1973), p. 85; Ronald W. Clark, *Einstein: The Life and Times* (New York: World Publishing Company, 1971), p. 120.

xii From now onwards: "Space and Time" lecture given at the 80th Meeting of Natural Scientists in Cologne, Germany, on September 21, 1908, in Hermann Minkowski, *Space and Time: Minkowski's Papers on Relativity,* ed. Vesselin Petkov, trans. Fritz Lewertoff and Vesselin Petkov (Montreal: Minkowski Institute Press, 2012), p. 111.

xii The representation of: Arthur Schopenhauer, *On the Fourfold Root of the Principle of Sufficient Reason*, trans. Mme. Karl Hillebrand (New York: Cosimo, 2007), p. 32.

xiv I saw in a dream: B.M. Kedrov, "On the Question of the Psychology of Scientific Creativity (On the Occasion of the Discovery by D.I. Mendeleev of the Periodic Law)," *Soviet Review* 8, no. 2 (Summer 1967), p. 38. This is an English translation of an earlier article which originally appeared in *Voprosy psikhologgi* 3, no. 6 (1957), pp. 91-113.

xv I awoke, turned on: Otto Loewi, "Autobiographical Sketch," *Perspectives in Biology and Medicine* 4, no. 1, (Autumn 1960) article reprinted in Josef Donnerer and Fred Lembeck, *The Chemical Languages of the Nervous System: History of Scientists and Substances* (Basel; New York: Karger, 2006), p. 22.

xv My poor brain: Letter from Richard Wagner to Mathilde Wesendonck, March 25, 1859, in Milan, quoted in Richard Wagner and Mathilde Wesendonck, *Richard Wagner to Mathilde Wesendonck,* trans. William Ashton Ellis (New York: Charles Scribner's Sons, 1905), p. 112.

xv I woke up with: Barry Miles, *Paul McCartney: Many Years From Now* (New York: H. Holt, 1997), pp. 201-202.

xv What terrified me: Mary Shelley, *Frankenstein, or The Modern Prometheus* (Boston: Sever, Francis & Company, 1869), p. 12.

xv I can never decide: D.H. Lawrence, *The Letters of D.H. Lawrence. Volume 1: 1901-13,* The Cambridge Edition, ed. James T. Boulton (Cambridge, England: Cambridge University Press, 2002), p. 359. Letter from Lawrence to Edward Garnett, January 29, 1912.

xvi There comes a point: William Miller, "Death of a Genius: His Fourth Dimension, Time, Overtakes Einstein," *Life* 38, no. 18 (May 2, 1955), p. 64.

xvi I claim credit for nothing: George Sylvester Viereck, "What Life Means to Einstein," *The Saturday Evening Post,* October 26, 1929, p. 117.

xvi dethroned time...a liberation from: Erwin Schrödinger, *Mind and Matter: The Tarner Lectures Delivered at Trinity College* (Cambridge, England: Cambridge University Press, 1958), p. 82.

xvii We were in the neighbor's: Louis Ferrante, *Unlocked: The Life and Crimes of a Mafia Insider* (New York: Harper Paperbacks, 2009), pp. 154-155.

3 "Oh, my God": Banesh Hoffmann, with the collaboration of Helen Dukas, *Albert Einstein: Creator and Rebel* (New York: Viking, 1973), p. 210.

11 A dream dreamt by Maury: Sigmund Freud, *The Interpretation of Dreams*, Eighth Edition, rev., trans. and ed. James Strachey (New York: Avon Books, 1965), p. 60.

12 This dream was the basis: Sigmund Freud, *The Interpretation of Dreams*, Eighth Edition, rev., trans. and ed. James Strachey (New York: Avon Books, 1965), p. 60.

13 Dreams such as the one: Sigmund Freud, *The Interpretation of Dreams*, Eighth Edition, rev., trans. and ed. James Strachey (New York: Avon Books, 1965), p. 97.

15 The brain decides to initiate: Benjamin Libet et al, "Time of Unconscious Intention to Act in Relation to Onset of Cerebral Activity (Readiness-Potential): The Unconscious Initiation of a Freely Voluntary Act," *Brain* 106 (1983), p. 640.

18 more than 3000 recollections: David Foulkes, Wilse B. Webb, and Rosalind D. Cartwright, *The New Encyclopaedia Britannica,* 15th Edition, "Sleep and Dreams" (Chicago: Encyclopaedia Britannica, 1991), 27:306.

18 accomplices awaken him: J. Allan Hobson, *The Dreaming Brain: How the Brain Creates Both the Sense and the Nonsense of Dreams* (New York: Basic Books, 1988), p. 33.

21 willing an act: Richard Restak, *The Brain: The Last Frontier* (New York: Warner Books, 1979), p. 244.

24 How many animals: Daniel Kahneman, *Thinking, Fast and Slow* (New York: Farrar, Straus, and Giroux, 2011), p. 73.

24 produce cognitive ease: Daniel Kahneman, *Thinking, Fast and Slow* (New York: Farrar, Straus, and Giroux, 2011), p. 73.

33-34 I always find it: Albrecht Folsing, *Albert Einstein: A Biography*, trans. Ewald Oser (New York: Viking, 1997), p. 651. Letter from Einstein to Freud, July 30, 1930.

34 I always envy the physicists: Ernest Jones, *The Life and Work of Sigmund Freud* (New York: Basic Books, 1957), 2:419. Letter from Freud to Marie Bonaparte.

34 took over the complicated: Ronald W. Clark, *Einstein: The Life and Times* (New York: World Publishing Company, 1971), p. 110.

34 I am now working exclusively: Albert Einstein, *The Collected Papers of Albert Einstein. The Swiss Years: Correspondence, 1902-1914*, trans. Anna Beck (Princeton, NJ: Princeton University Press., 1995), 5:324. Letter from Einstein to Arnold Sommerfeld, October 29, 1912.

34-35 Since the mathematicians: From the essay, "To Albert Einstein's Seventieth Birthday," by Arnold Sommerfeld, in Albert Einstein, *Albert Einstein: Philosopher-Scientist*, ed. Paul Arthur Schilpp, Volume VII in the Library of Living Philosophers (New York: MJF Books, 1970), p. 102.

36 I have observed stars: Thomas Campbell, *The Life and Letters of Thomas Campbell*, ed. William Beattie (London: Hall, Virtue, and Company, 1850), 2:235-236. Letter written by Campbell, September 15, 1813.

38 It may not always be: George Sylvester Viereck, "What Life Means to Einstein," *The Saturday Evening Post,* October 26, 1929, p. 114.

38 descended to the underworld: R.D. Laing, *The Divided Self* (New York: Pantheon Books, 1960), p. 24.

38 the knowledge he brought back: R.D. Laing, *The Divided Self* (New York: Pantheon Books, 1960), p. 24.

40 The boy will come: Sigmund Freud, *The Interpretation of Dreams*, Eighth Edition, rev, trans. and ed. James Strachey (New York: Avon Books, 1965), p. 250.

41 It doesn't matter: Ronald W. Clark, *Einstein: The Life and Times* (New York: World Publishing Company, 1971), p. 10.

41 This was all so abstract: Albert Einstein, *Einstein: The Man and His Achievements*, ed. G.J. Whitrow (New York: Dover, 1967), p. 43.

41 bad reception: Sigmund Freud, *An Autobiographical Study*, trans. and ed. James Strachey (London: Hogarth Press, 1948), p. 25.

41 banged his fist: Ernest Jones, *The Life and Work of Sigmund Freud* (New York: Basic Books, 1957), 2:109.

42 There is something blocking: Albrecht Folsing, *Albert Einstein: A Biography*, trans. Ewald Oser (New York: Viking, 1997), p. 731, as quoted in Walter Isaacson, *Einstein: His Life and Universe* (New York: Simon & Schuster Paperbacks, 2007), p. 516. Letter Einstein to Carl Seelig, January 4, 1954. Translations vary, I chose Isaacson.

42 This is my post: Ernest Jones, *The Life and Work of Sigmund Freud* (New York: Basic Books, 1957), 1:294.

42 I didn't know: Ronald W. Clark, *Einstein: The Life and Times* (New York: World Publishing Company, 1971), p. 494.

43 toward the end of his: Palle Yourgrau, *A World Without Time: The Forgotten Legacy of Gödel and Einstein* (New York: Basic Books, 2005), p. 148.

43 [Einstein] understands as much: Sigmund Freud and Sándor Ferenczi, *The Correspondence of Sigmund Freud and Sándor Ferenczi: Volume 3, 1920-1933*, ed. Ernst Falzeder and Eva Brabant, with the collaboration of Patrizia Giampieri-Deutsch, trans. Peter T. Hoffer (Cambridge, MA: Belknap Press of Harvard University Press, 2000), p. 292. Letter from Freud to Ferenczi, January 2, 1927.

43 always reforms itself: Sigmund Freud and Sándor Ferenczi, *The Correspondence of Sigmund Freud and Sándor Ferenczi: Volume 1, 1908-1914*, ed. Ernst Falzeder, Eva Brabant, and Patrizia Giampieri-Deutsch, trans. by Peter T. Hoffer (Cambridge, MA: Belknap Press of Harvard University Press, 1993), p. 79. Letter from Freud to Ferenczi, October 6, 1909.

44 The processes of the: From "The Unconscious," trans. Cecil M. Baines, 1915, in Sigmund Freud, *Sigmund Freud: Collected Papers*, Authorized Translation Under the Supervision of Joan Riviere (New York: Basic Books, 1959), 4:119.

44 these are dangerous expeditions: Sigmund Freud and Sándor Ferenczi, *The Correspondence of Sigmund Freud and Sándor Ferenczi: Volume 1, 1908-1914*, ed. Ernst Falzeder, Eva Brabant, and Patrizia Giampieri-Deutsch, trans. Peter T. Hoffer (Cambridge, MA: Belknap Press of Harvard University Press, 1993), p. 274. Letter from Freud to Ferenczi, May 11, 1911.

44-45 I advise you against: Sigmund Freud and Sándor Ferenczi, *The Correspondence of Sigmund Freud and Sándor Ferenczi: Volume 3, 1920-1933*, ed. Ernst Falzeder and Eva Brabant, with the collaboration of Patrizia Giampieri-Deutsch, trans. Peter T. Hoffer (Cambridge, MA: Belknap Press of Harvard University Press, 2000), p. 209. Letter from Freud to Ferenczi, March 25, 1925.

45 is my private affair: Ernest Jones, *The Life and Work of Sigmund* Freud (New York: Basic Books, 1957), 3:395. Letter from Freud to Jones, March 7, 1926.

47-48 A few days after: Sigmund Freud, *The Psychopathology of Everyday Life,* The Standard Edition, trans. and ed. James Strachey (New York: W.W. Norton & Company, 1965), p. 336.

49 When Freud read: Ernest Jones, *The Life and Work of Sigmund Freud* (New York: Basic Books, 1957), 2:14.

50 You will know that: From "Dreams and Telepathy," trans. C.J.M. Hubback, 1922, in Sigmund Freud, *Sigmund Freud: Collected Papers*, Authorized Translation Under the Supervision of Joan Riviere (New York: Basic Books, 1959), 4:408.

50 And if the existence: From "Dreams and Telepathy," trans. C.J.M. Hubback, 1922, in Sigmund Freud, *Sigmund Freud: Collected Papers*, Authorized Translation Under the Supervision of Joan Riviere (New York: Basic Books, 1959), 4:408.

50 My son, however: From "Dreams and Telepathy," trans. C.J.M. Hubback, 1922, in Sigmund Freud, *Sigmund Freud: Collected Papers*, Authorized Translation Under the Supervision of Joan Riviere (New York: Basic Books, 1959), 4:409.

50 Despite many hazardous: Ernest Jones, *The Life and Work of Sigmund Freud* (New York: Basic Books, 1957), 2:191.

50 Freud's *favorite sister*: Ernest Jones, *The Life and Work of Sigmund Freud* (New York: Basic Books, 1957), 2:191.

50-51 My sister's: Sigmund Freud and Karl Abraham, *The Complete Correspondence of Sigmund Freud and Karl Abraham: 1907-1925: Complete Edition,* ed. Ernst Falzeder, trans. by Caroline Schwarzacher, with the collaboration of Christine Trollope and Klara Majthenyi King (London: Karnac Books, 2002), p. 353. Letter #319F from Freud to Abraham, July 13, 1917.

51 a few days later: Peter Gay, *Freud: A Life for Our Time* (New York: W.W. Norton & Company, 1988), p.354.

51-52 The notion that there is: From "The Occult Significance of Dreams," trans. James Strachey, 1925, in Sigmund Freud, *Sigmund Freud: Collected Papers,* Authorized Translation Under the Supervision of Joan Riviere (New York: Basic Books, 1959), 5:159.

53 The only real revolution: Will and Ariel Durant, *The Lessons of History* (New York: Simon & Schuster, 1968), p. 72.

53 solitary, poor, nasty: Thomas Hobbes, *Leviathan*, in
Great Books of the Western World, "Machiavelli
Hobbes," Editor in Chief Robert Maynard Hutchins
(Chicago: Encyclopaedia Britannica, 1952), 23:85.

54 strictly secret: Sigmund Freud and Ernest Jones, *The
Complete Correspondence of Sigmund Freud and Ernest
Jones, 1908-1939,* ed. R. Andrew Paskauskas
(Cambridge, MA: Belknap Press of Harvard University
Press, 1993), p. 148. Letter from Freud to Jones, August
1, 1912.

54 to guard the kingdom: Sigmund Freud and Ernest
Jones, *The Complete Correspondence of Sigmund Freud
and Ernest Jones, 1908-1939,* ed. R. Andrew Paskauskas
(Cambridge, MA: Belknap Press of Harvard University
Press, 1993), p. 149. Letter from Jones to Freud, August
7, 1912.

55 Your Majesty's communication: Otto Prince von
Bismarck, *Bismarck: The Man and the Statesman: Being
the Reflections and Reminiscences of Otto Prince Von
Bismarck*, trans. A.J. Butler (Leipzig, Germany: Bernhard
Tauchnitz, 1899), 3:132, as quoted in Sigmund Freud, *The
Interpretation of Dreams*, Eighth Edition, rev., trans. and
ed. James Strachey (New York: Avon Books, 1965), p.
413.

56 the dreamer with whom: Sigmund Freud, *The
Interpretation of Dreams*, Eighth Edition, rev., trans. and
ed. James Strachey (New York: Avon Books, 1965), p.
414.

56 that [Bismarck] took: Sigmund Freud, *The
Interpretation of Dreams*, Eighth Edition, rev., trans. and
ed. James Strachey (New York: Avon Books, 1965), p.
415.

56 an infantile masturbation: Sigmund Freud, *The Interpretation of Dreams*, Eighth Edition, rev., trans. and ed. James Strachey (New York: Avon Books, 1965), p. 416.

57 My emotional life: Sigmund Freud, *The Interpretation of Dreams*, Eighth Edition, rev., trans. and ed. James Strachey (New York: Avon Books, 1965), pg. 521.

57 [Freud] could both love: Ernest Jones, *The Life and Work of Sigmund Freud* (New York: Basic Books, 1957), 1:162.

57 friendships follow the same: Erich Fromm, *Sigmund Freud's Mission: An Analysis of His Personality and Influence* (New York: Harper & Brothers, 1959), p. 38.

57 Hannibal had a place: Sigmund Freud, *The Interpretation of Dreams*, Eighth Edition, rev., trans. and ed. James Strachey (New York: Avon Books, 1965), p. 230.

57 had powerfully attracted: Sigmund Freud, *The Interpretation of Dreams*, Eighth Edition, rev., trans. and ed. James Strachey (New York: Avon Books, 1965), p. 484.

57-58 remember sticking labels: Sigmund Freud, *The Interpretation of Dreams*, Eighth Edition, rev., trans. and ed. James Strachey (New York: Avon Books, 1965), p. 230.

58 The Franco-Prussian War: Ernest Jones, *The Life and Work of Sigmund Freud* (New York: Basic Books, 1957), 1:23.

58 such an ardent admirer: Ernest Jones, *The Life and Work of Sigmund Freud* (New York: Basic Books, 1957), 1:192.

58 there were many links: Ernest Jones, *The Life and Work of Sigmund Freud* (New York: Basic Books, 1957), 1:192.

59 When the great man: Ernest Jones, *The Life and Work of Sigmund Freud* (New York: Basic Books, 1957), 1:192.

59 behavior one would have: Ernest Jones, *The Life and Work of Sigmund Freud* (New York: Basic Books, 1957), 1:192.

59 harder than any other: Sigmund Freud, *The Origins of Psycho-Analysis: Letters to Wilhelm Fliess, Drafts, and Notes*, ed. Marie Bonaparte, Anna Freud, and Ernest Kris, trans. Eric Mosbacher and James Strachey (New York: Basic Books, 1950), p. 214. Letter from Freud to Fliess, August 14, 1897.

59 as a means of: Ernest Jones, *The Life and Work of Sigmund Freud* (New York: Basic Books, 1957), 1:356. Letter from Freud to Fliess.

59 reaction to my: Sigmund Freud, *The Interpretation of Dreams*, Eighth Edition, rev., trans. and ed. James Strachey (New York: Avon Books, 1965), p. xxvi.

59 The path ended in: Ernest Jones, *The Life and Work of Sigmund Freud* (New York: Basic Books, 1957), 1:307.

60 to find a father-substitute: Ernest Jones, *The Life and Work of Sigmund Freud* (New York: Basic Books, 1957), 1:307.

60 swelling undercurrent: Ernest Jones, *The Life and Work of Sigmund Freud* (New York: Basic Books, 1957), 1:324.

64 There is but a: Louis Antoine Fauvelet de Bourrienne and Napoleon, Emperor of France, *Memoirs of Napoleon Bonaparte*, ed. R.W. Phipps (London: Richard Bentley, 1836), 3:226.

64-65 I never was truly: Emmanuel-Auguste-Dieudonné Las Cases, *Mémorial de Sainte Hélène: Journal of the Private Life and Conversations of the Emperor Napoleon at Saint Helena* (London: Henry Colburn & Company, 1823), 4:133.

65 Man cannot create: A.J.P. Taylor, *Bismarck: The Man and the Statesman* (New York: Vintage Books, 1967), p. 70.

65 His survival was all: Edward Crankshaw, *Bismarck* (New York: Viking, 1981), pp. 131-132.

65 revolutionizing the map: A.J.P. Taylor, *Bismarck: The Man and the Statesman* (New York: Vintage Books, 1967), p. 63.

65 the French would do: A.J.P. Taylor, *Bismarck: The Man and the Statesman* (New York: Vintage Books, 1967), p. 64.

66 came to realize: A.J.P. Taylor, *Bismarck: The Man and the Statesman* (New York: Vintage Books, 1967), p. 65.

67 compared the king to a *horse*: A.J.P. Taylor, *Bismarck: The Man and the Statesman* (New York: Vintage Books, 1967), p. 56.

67 [Bismarck] compared the king: Erich Eyck, *Bismarck and the German Empire* (New York: W.W. Norton & Company, 1968), p. 58.

67-68 In June 1866: Edward Crankshaw, *Bismarck* (New York: Viking, 1981), p. 179.

68 Napoleon le Petit: Graham Robb, *Victor Hugo: A Biography* (New York: W.W. Norton & Company, 1997), p. 290. From a political speech Hugo gave in the French Assembly, July 17, 1851.

68 Napoleon le Grand: Graham Robb, *Victor Hugo: A Biography* (New York: W.W. Norton & Company, 1997), p. 290. From a political speech Hugo gave in the French Assembly, July 17, 1851.

68 living space: Adolf Hitler, *Mein Kampf*, trans. Ralph Manheim (New York: Houghton Mifflin Company, 1971), p. 646.

68 Bolshevik menace: Franz Halder, *Kriegstagebuch,* as quoted in Norman Rich, *Hitler's War Aims: Ideology, the Nazi State, and the Course of Expansion* (New York: W.W. Norton & Company, 1973), p. 217.

69 The whole episode: Sigmund Freud, *The Interpretation of Dreams*, Eighth Edition, rev., trans. and ed. James Strachey (New York: Avon Books, 1965), p. 415.

69 But on the other hand: Sigmund Freud, *The Interpretation of Dreams*, Eighth Edition, rev., trans. and ed. James Strachey (New York: Avon Books, 1965), p. 415.

71 in anxiety ridden: *The Oxford Companion to the Mind*, ed. Richard L. Gregory (New York: Oxford University Press, 1987), p. 202.

73 Belief that did not: Albert Einstein, *Out of My Later Years* (New York: Philosophical Library, 1950), p. 21. From an address at Princeton Theological Seminary, May 19, 1939.

78 Dreams are guardians: Sigmund Freud, *The Interpretation of Dreams*, Eighth Edition, rev., trans. and ed. James Strachey (New York: Avon Books, 1965), p. 267.

84 destroyed the Tsar's: John Keegan, *The First World War* (New York: Alfred A. Knopf, 1999), pp. 411-412.

84-85 I wouldn't dream of: Martin Gilbert, *The First World War: A Complete History* (New York: Henry Holt and Company, 1994), p. 490.

85 had degenerated into: Richard M. Watt, *The Kings Depart: The Tragedy of Germany: Versailles and the German Revolution* (New York: Simon & Schuster, 1968), p. 188.

85 Good-bye to all: Title of Robert Graves' memoir, *Good-Bye to All That: An Autobiography*, New Edition, Revised (New York: Anchor Books, 1998).

85 November Criminals: Alan Bullock, *Hitler: A Study in Tyranny* (New York: Konecky & Konecky, 1962), p. 58.

85 a state of psychic: Albert Einstein, *Ideas and Opinions: Based on Mein Weltbild*, ed. Carl Seelig and Other Sources, new trans. and rev. by Sonja Bargmann (New York: Crown, 1954), p. 207. Letter from Einstein to the Prussian Academy of Science, April 5, 1933.

86 long succession of: From "Recapitulation," in François Marie Arouet de Voltaire, *The Portable Voltaire*, ed. Ben Ray Redman (New York: Penguin Books, 1977), p. 549.

86 Modern physics is: William L. Shirer, *The Rise and Fall of the Third Reich: A History of Nazi Germany* (New York: MJF Books, 1988), p. 525.

86 became a bitter: Albert Einstein, *Albert Einstein: The Human Side, Glimpses from His Archives*, ed. Helen Dukas and Banesh Hoffmann (Princeton, NJ: Princeton University Press, 1979), p. 20.

86 advocated the view: Philipp Frank, *Einstein: His Life and Times,* trans. George Rosen, ed. and rev. Shuichi Kusaka (New York: Da Capo Press, [1989] 1947), p. 238.

86 German physicists accepted: Philipp Frank, *Einstein: His Life and Times,* trans. George Rosen, ed. and rev. Shuichi Kusaka (New York: Da Capo Press, [1989] 1947), p. 238.

86 Jewish wives: Philipp Frank, *Einstein: His Life and Times*, trans. George Rosen, ed. and rev. Shuichi Kusaka (New York: Da Capo Press, [1989] 1947), p. 238.

86 chief function: Ernest Jones, *The Life and Work of Sigmund Freud* (New York: Basic Books, 1957), 3:186.

87-88 If the dismissal: Walter Isaacson, *Einstein: His Life and Universe* (New York: Simon & Schuster Paperbacks, 2007), p. 407-408.

92 experimental science: Roger Bacon, "On Experimental Science," from *Opus Majus,* in *Moments of Discovery: Volume 1: The Origins of Science*, ed. George Schwartz and Philip W. Bishop (New York: Basic Books, 1958), 1:28.

92 two modes of acquiring: Roger Bacon, "On Experimental Science," from *Opus Majus,* in *Moments of Discovery: Volume 1: The Origins of Science*, ed. George Schwartz and Philip W. Bishop (New York: Basic Books, 1958), 1:28.

92 the art of logic: Francis Bacon, *Novum Organum*, in *Great Books of the Western World*, "Francis Bacon," Editor in Chief Robert Maynard Hutchins (Chicago: Encyclopaedia Britannica, 1952), 30:105.

92 As a boy of twelve: Alice Calaprice and Trevor Lipscombe, *Albert Einstein: A Biography* (Westport, CT: Greenwood Press, 2005), p. 7. From an interview of Einstein with Henry Russo, for *The Tower*, a Princeton High School newspaper, April 13, 1935.

92 All knowledge of reality: Albert Einstein, *Ideas and Opinions: Based on Mein Weltbild*, ed. Carl Seelig and Other Sources, new trans. and rev. Sonja Bargmann (New York: Crown, 1954), p. 271. From the speech, "On the Method of Theoretical Physics," The Herbert Spencer Lecture, delivered at Oxford, June 10, 1933.

93 fears regarding: Carl Seelig, *Albert Einstein: A Documentary Biography,* trans. Mervyn Savill (London: Staples Press, 1956), p. 102, as quoted in Walter Isaacson, *Einstein: His Life and Universe* (New York: Simon & Schuster Paperbacks, 2007), p. 161. Letter from Einstein to Arnold Sommerfeld, January 19, 1909.

93 pick up a piece: Albrecht Folsing, *Albert Einstein: A Biography,* trans. Ewald Oser (New York: Viking, 1997), p. 264. Freud dialogue with Hans Tanner.

93 I recommended: Max Talmey, *The Relativity Theory Simplified and the Formative Years of Its Inventor* (New York: Falcon Press, 1932), p. 164.

94 The beautiful harmony: Banesh Hoffmann with the collaboration of Helen Dukas, *Albert Einstein: Creator and Rebel* (New York: Viking, 1973), p. 195. Letter from Einstein to Navy Ensign Guy H. Raner, Jr., July 2, 1945. Letter available at: http://www.shapell.org/manuscript.aspx?einstein-agnostic-atheism-religion

95 people could not: Ronald W. Clark, *Einstein: The Life and Times* (New York: World Publishing Company, 1971), p. 106.

95 the greatest thing: Banesh Hoffmann with the collaboration of Helen Dukas, *Albert Einstein: Creator and Rebel* (New York: Viking, 1973), p. 36.

95 By being deliberately: Banesh Hoffmann with the collaboration of Helen Dukas, *Albert Einstein: Creator and Rebel* (New York: Viking, 1973), p. 42.

95 In conclusion: Arthur J. Miller, *Albert Einstein's Special Theory of Relativity: Emergence (1905) and Early Interpretation, (1905-1911)* (New York: Springer Verlag, 1998), p. 393. Translation of entire speech/paper is in the Appendix of Miller's book.

96 splendid isolation: Sigmund Freud, *On the History of the Psycho-Analytic Movement*, rev. and ed. James Strachey, trans. Joan Riviere (New York: W.W. Norton & Company, 1966), p. 22.

96 I am actually not: Sigmund Freud, *The Complete Letters of Sigmund Freud to Wilhelm Fliess, 1887-1904*, ed. and trans. Jeffrey Moussaieff Masson (Cambridge, MA: Belknap Press, 1985), p. 398. Letter from Freud to Fliess, February 1, 1900.

98 caliper measurements: Sandra F. Witelson, Debra L. Kigar, and Thomas Harvey, "The Exceptional Brain of Albert Einstein," *Lancet* 353, no. 9170, (1999), p. 2149.

98 calibrated photographs: Sandra F. Witelson, Debra L. Kigar, and Thomas Harvey, "The Exceptional Brain of Albert Einstein," *Lancet* 353, no. 9170, (1999) p. 2149.

98 into approximately 240: Sandra F. Witelson, Debra L. Kigar, and Thomas Harvey, "The Exceptional Brain of Albert Einstein," *Lancet* 353, no. 9170, (1999), p. 2149.

98 his brain weight: Sandra F. Witelson, Debra L. Kigar, and Thomas Harvey, "The Exceptional Brain of Albert Einstein," *Lancet* 353, no. 9170, (1999), p. 2151.

98 brain length, size: Sandra F. Witelson, Debra L. Kigar, and Thomas Harvey, "The Exceptional Brain of Albert Einstein," *Lancet* 353, no. 9170, (1999) p. 2151.

98 in the parietal: Sandra F. Witelson, Debra L. Kigar, and Thomas Harvey, "The Exceptional Brain of Albert Einstein," *Lancet* 353, no. 9170, (1999), p. 2151.

98 A man can do: Translation of "What I will, I can do, and I will what I will." Arthur Schopenhauer, *Essay on Freedom of the Will,* Dover Philosophical Classics Series, trans. Konstantin Kolenda (Mineola, NY: Dover, 2005), p. 21, as quoted in Albert Einstein, *Ideas and Opinions: Based on Mein Weltbild,* ed. Carl Seelig and Other Sources, trans. and rev. Sonja Bargmann (New York: Crown, 1954), p. 8. From "The World As I See It."

99 It ought to be: Charles G. Gross, "Aristotle on the Brain," *The Neuroscientist* 1, no. 4, (July 1995), p. 246.

99 In what part does: From "On Dreams, That They are God-Sent," in Philo, *The Works of Philo: Complete and Unabridged in One Volume,* trans. C.D. Yonge (Peabody, MA: Hendrickson Publishers, 1993), pp. 367-368.

100 That our being: Sir Charles Sherrington, *The Integrative Action of the Nervous System*, Second Edition (New Haven, CT: Yale University Press, 1947), p. xxiv.

100 Minds are simply: Marvin Minsky, *The Society of Mind* (New York: Simon & Schuster, 1986), p. 287.

100 I reject the concept: Wilder Penfield, *The Mystery of the Mind: A Critical Study of Consciousness and the Human Brain* (Princeton, NJ: Princeton University Press, 1975) p. 114.

101 Every theory is: Einstein to Viscount Herbert Samuel, February 5, 1923, as quoted in Ronald W. Clark, *Einstein: The Life and Times* (New York: World Publishing Company, 1971), p. 624.

101 I hate Vienna: Sigmund Freud, *The Origins of Psycho-Analysis: Sigmund Freud's Letters, Drafts, and Notes to Wilhelm Fliess, 1887-1902*, ed. Marie Bonaparte, Anna Freud, and Ernest Kris, trans. Eric Mosbacher and James Strachey (New York: Basic Books, 1977), p. 311. Letter from Freud to Fliess, March 11, 1900.

105 Let me see your Glory: Book of Exodus, 33:18, in *The Five Books of Moses: Genesis, Exodus, Leviticus, Numbers, and Deuteronomy. The Schocken Bible*, trans. Everett Fox (New York: Schocken Books, 1995), 1:452.

105 You cannot see: Book of Exodus, 33:20, in *The Five Books of Moses: Genesis, Exodus, Leviticus, Numbers, and Deuteronomy. The Schocken Bible*, trans. Everett Fox (New York: Schocken Books, 1995), 1:452.

105 I will place you: Book of Exodus, 33:2, in *The Five Books of Moses: Genesis, Exodus, Leviticus, Numbers, and Deuteronomy. The Schocken Bible*, trans. Everett Fox (New York: Schocken Books, 1995), 1:453.

105 passed before [Moses]: Book of Exodus, 34:6, in *The Five Books of Moses: Genesis, Exodus, Leviticus, Numbers, and Deuteronomy. The Schocken Bible*, trans. Everett Fox (New York: Schocken Books, 1995), 1:455.

105 the skin on [Moses]: Book of Exodus, 34:35, in *The Five Books of Moses: Genesis, Exodus, Leviticus, Numbers, and Deuteronomy. The Schocken Bible*, trans. Everett Fox (New York: Schocken Books, 1995), 1:460.

108 I could see about: Kary Mullis, NPR *Science Friday* Radio Interview, May 21, 1999. http://www.sciencefriday.com/segment/05/21/1999/kary-mullis.html

108 What seems to be: Brian Josephson, quoted in "Is This Really Proof That Man Can See Into the Future?" *Daily Mail*, London, May 4, 2007. http://www.dailymail.co.uk/sciencetech/article-452833/Is-REALLY-proof-man-future.html

109 in advance significantly: S. James P. Spottiswoode, and E.C. May, "Skin Conductance Prestimulus Response: Analyses, Artifacts, and a Pilot Study," *Journal of Scientific Exploration* 17, no. 4 (2003), p. 618.

109 More than forty: Julia Mossbridge, Patrizio Tressoldi, and Jessica Utts, "Predictive Physiological Anticipation Preceding Seemingly Unpredictable Stimuli," *Frontiers in Psychology* 3, Article 390 (October 17, 2012), p. 1.

110 There seems to be: Julia Mossbridge, Patrizio Tressoldi, and Jessica Utts, "Predictive Physiological Anticipation Preceding Seemingly Unpredictable Stimuli," *Frontiers in Psychology* 3, Article 390 (October 17, 2012), p. 10.

110 Sleep is an essential: Dr. Hildegard Niemann and Dr. Christian Maschke, "WHO LARES: Final Report Noise Effects and Morbidity." (Copenhagen, Denmark: WHO Regional Office for Europe. 2004), pp. 12-14.

110 Sleep can be severely: Dr. Hildegard Niemann and Dr. Christian Maschke, "WHO LARES: Final Report Noise Effects and Morbidity." (Copenhagen, Denmark: WHO Regional Office for Europe. 2004), p. 19.

111 pupillary dilation: Dean Radin and Ana Borges, "Intuition Through Time: What Does the Seer See?" *Explore* 5, no. 4 (July/August 2009), p. 200.

115 a vast domain: *Mind and Brain*, ed. Time-Life
Books (Alexandria, VA: Time-Life Books, 1993), p. 84.

115 the grand master: *Mind and Brain*, ed. Time-Life
Books (Alexandria, VA: Time-Life Books, 1993), p. 83.

116 An increase in: *Mind and Brain*, ed. Time-Life
Books (Alexandria, VA: Time-Life Books, 1993), p. 91.

119 the amygdala, an almond: Jeffrey Sutton as quoted
in William J. Cromie, "Research Links Sleep, Dreams,
and Learning," *The Harvard University Gazette*, February
8, 1996.
http://www.news.harvard.edu/gazette/1996/02.08/Researc
hLinksSl.html

119 operates unconsciously: Rita Carter et al., *The
Human Brain Book* (New York: DK Publishing, 2009), p.
125.

119-120 A frightening sight: Rita Carter et al., *The
Human Brain Book* (New York: DK Publishing, 2009), p.
125.

120 threat center: Rita Carter et al., *The Human Brain
Book* (New York: DK Publishing, 2009), p. 125.

120 registers the emotional: Rita Carter et al., *The
Human Brain Book* (New York: DK Publishing, 2009), p.
125.

120 unconscious presentation of negative: Ulf Dimberg,
Monika Thunberg, and Kurt Elmehed, "Research Report:
Unconscious Facial Reactions to Emotional Facial
Expressions," *Psychological Science* 11, no. 1 (January
2000), p. 89.

120 an involvement of: David Sander, Jordan Grafman, and Tiziana Zalla, "The Human Amygdala: An Evolved System for Relevance Detection," *Reviews in the Neurosciences* 14, no. 4 (2003), p. 307.

121 the human amygdala: Justin S. Feinstein et al., "The Human Amygdala and the Induction and Experience of Fear," *Current Biology* 21 (January 11, 2011), p. 34.

121 Her behavior: Justin S. Feinstein et al., "The Human Amygdala and the Induction and Experience of Fear," *Current Biology* 21 (January 11, 2011), p. 37.

122 evidence for the role: Jan Glascher and Ralph Adolphs, "Processing of the Arousal of Subliminal and Supraliminal Emotional Stimuli by the Human Amygdala," *The Journal of Neuroscience* 23, no. 32 (November 12, 2003), p. 10274.

122 the amygdala was activated: David Sander, Jordan Grafman, and Tiziana Zalla, "The Human Amygdala: An Evolved System for Relevance Detection," *Reviews in the Neurosciences* 14, no. 4 (2003), p. 307.

122 the amygdala may play: Chiara M. Portas et al., "Auditory Processing Across the Sleep-Wake Cycle: Simultaneous EEG and fMRI Monitoring in Humans," *Neuron* 28, no.3 (December 2000), p. 994.

124 What always fascinated: Andrea Rock, *The Mind at Night: The New Science of How and Why We Dream* (New York: Basic Books, 2004), p. 121.

124-125 a third state: Michel Jouvet, *The Paradox of Sleep: The Story of Dreaming*, trans. Laurence Garey (Cambridge, MA: MIT Press, 1999), p. 5.

125 We must be prepared: From "The Unconscious," trans. Cecil M. Baines, in Sigmund Freud, *Sigmund Freud: Collected Papers*, Authorized Translation Under the Supervision of Joan Riviere (New York: Basic Books, 1959), 4:103.

131 the future exists: *Question of Time: The Ultimate Paradox*, ed. of *Scientific American*, 2012. From "Introduction: What Time Is It?"

131 the only one of: Freeman J. Dyson, *From Eros to Gaia* (New York: Penguin Books, 1993), p. 161.

131 proved, from the: Palle Yourgrau, *A World Without Time: The Forgotten Legacy of Gödel and Einstein* (New York: Basic Books, 2005), pg. 6.

132 I have got a few: Carl Seelig, *Albert Einstein: A Documentary Biography*, trans. Mervyn Savill (London: Staples Press, 1956), p. 53. Letter from Einstein to Marcel Grossmann, April 14, 1901.

132 It would be extremely desirable: From a 1911 paper, "The Influence of Gravity on the Propagation of Light," as quoted in Philipp Frank, *Einstein: His Life and Times,* trans. George Rosen, ed. and rev. Shuichi Kusaka (New York: Da Capo Press, [1989] 1947), p. 97.

133 I knew the theory: Ilse Rosenthal-Schneider, *Relativity and Scientific Truth: Discussions with Einstein, Von Laue, and Planck* (Detroit, IL: Wayne State University Press, 1980), p. 74.

133 since no experiment: Thomas S. Kuhn, *The Structure of Scientific Revolutions*, Third Edition (Chicago: University of Chicago Press, 1996), p. 87.

134 even if they: Brian Greene, *The Fabric of the Cosmos: Space, Time, and the Texture of Reality* (New York: Alfred A. Knopf, 2004), p. 80.

134 spooky actions: Albert Einstein, Hedwig Born, and Max Born, *The Born-Einstein Letters: Correspondence between Albert Einstein and Max and Hedwig Born from 1916 to 1955 with Commentaries by Max Born,* trans. Irene Born (London: Macmillan, 1971), p. 158.

134 It is not possible: Eugene Wigner, *Remarks on the Mind-Body Question,* in *Quantum Theory and Measurement,* ed. John Archibald Wheeler and Wojciech Hubert Zurek (Princeton, NJ: Princeton University Press, 1983), p. 169.

134-135 I do not mean: H.G. Wells, *The Time Machine, and The Invisible Man* (New York: Barnes and Noble Classics, 2003), p. 3.

135 It remains for us: H.G. Wells, *The Time Machine, and The Invisible Man,* (New York: Barnes and Noble Classics, 2003), p. 94.

Bibliography

Baldwin, Neil. *Edison: Inventing the Century*. Chicago: University of Chicago Press, 2001.

Barrett, Deirdre. *The Committee of Sleep: How Artists, Scientists, and Athletes Use Dreams for Creative Problem-Solving—and You Can Too*. New York: Crown Publishers, 2001.

Bernstein, Jeremy. *Albert Einstein and the Frontiers of Physics*. New York: Oxford University Press, 1996.

Bismarck, Otto Prince von. *Bismarck: The Man and the Statesman: Being the Reflections and Reminiscences of Otto Prince Von Bismarck*. Translated by A. J. Butler. Vol. 3 Leipzig, Germany: Bernhard Tauchnitz, 1899.

Bodanis, David. *E=mc²: A Biography of the World's Most Famous Equation*. New York: Berkley Books, 2000.

Bourrienne, Louis Antoine Fauvelet de, and Napoleon, Emperor of France. *The Memoirs of Napoleon Bonaparte*. Edited by R.W. Phipps. Vol. 3 London: Richard Bentley, 1836.

Bruno, Giordano. *Cause, Principle and Unity: And Essays on Magic*. Edited and Translated by Richard J. Blackwell and Robert de Lucca. Cambridge, England: Cambridge University Press, 1998.

Bullock, Alan. *Hitler: A Study in Tyranny*. New York: Konecky & Konecky, 1962.

Calaprice, Alice, and Trevor Lipscombe. *Albert Einstein: A Biography*. Westport, CT: Greenwood Press, 2005.

Campbell, Thomas. *The Life and Letters of Thomas Campbell*. Edited by William Beattie. Vol. 2. London: Hall, Virtue, and Company, 1850.

Cannon, Walter. *Bodily Changes in Pain, Hunger, Fear, and Rage: An Account of Recent Researches Into the Function of Emotional Excitement*. New York: Appleton and Co., 1929.

Carter, Rita. *Mapping the Mind*. Berkeley, CA: University of California Press, 1999.

Carter, Rita, et al. *The Human Brain Book*. New York: DK Publishing, 2009.

Clark, Ronald W. *Einstein: The Life and Times*. New York: World Publishing Company, 1971.

Crankshaw, Edward. *Bismarck*. New York: Viking Press, 1981.

Cronin, Vincent. *Napoleon*. London: HarperCollins Publishers, 1994.

---. *The View from Planet Earth: Man Looks at the Cosmos*. New York: Quill, 1983.

Damasio, Antonio. *The Feeling of What Happens: Body and Emotion in the Making of Consciousness*. New York: Harcourt, Inc., 1999.

Diamond, Edwin. *The Science of Dreams*. New York: MacFadden Book, 1963.

Donnerer, Josef, and Fred Lembeck. *The Chemical Languages of the Nervous System: History of Scientists and Substances*. Basel, Switzerland: S. Karger AG Pub., 2006.

Dossey, Larry. *The Science of Premonitions: How Knowing the Future Can Help Us Avoid Danger, Maximize Opportunities, and Create a Better Life*. New York: Plume, 2009.

Dunne, J.W. *An Experiment with Time*. Charlottesville, VA: Hampton Roads Publishing, 2001.

Durant, Will, and Ariel. *The Age of Voltaire: A History of Civilization in Western Europe from 1715 to 1756, With Special Emphasis on the Conflict Between Religion and Philosophy. Part IX: The Story of Civilization*. New York: Simon & Schuster, 1965.

---. *The Lessons of History*. New York: Simon & Schuster, 1968.

Dyson, Freeman J. *From Eros to Gaia*. New York: Penguin Books, 1993.

Eddington, Sir Arthur Stanley. *Space, Time, and Gravitation: An Outline of the General Theory of Relativity*. New York: Cambridge University Press, 1987, 1920.

Einstein, Albert. *Albert Einstein: The Human Side: Glimpses From His Archives*. Edited by Helen Dukas and Banesh Hoffmann. New Jersey: Princeton University Press, 2013.

---. *Albert Einstein: Philosopher-Scientist. Library of Living Philosophers.* Edited by Paul Arthur Schilpp. Vol. 7 New York: MJF Books, 1970.

---. *The Collected Papers of Albert Einstein. The Swiss Years: Correspondence, 1902-1914.* Translated by Anna Beck. Vol. 5 Princeton, NJ: Princeton University Press, 1995.

---. *Einstein: The Man and His Achievements.* Edited by G.J. Whitrow. New York: Dover, 1967.

---. *Ideas and Opinions: Based on Mein Weltbild.* Edited by Carl Seelig and Other Sources. New Translations and Revisions by Sonja Bargmann. New York: Crown Publishers, 1954.

---. *Out of My Later Years.* New York: Philosophical Library, 1950.

---. *The Quotable Einstein.* Edited by Alice Calaprice. Princeton, NJ: Princeton University Press, 1996.

---. *Relativity: The Special and the General Theory.* 100th Anniversary Edition. Authorized Translation by Robert W. Lawson. New York: Tess Press, 2005.

Einstein, Albert, Hedwig Born, and Max Born. *The Born-Einstein Letters: Correspondence Between Albert Einstein and Max and Hedwig Born from 1916 to 1955 with Commentaries by Max Born.* Translated by Irene Born. London: Macmillan, 1971.

Eyck, Erich. *Bismarck and the German Empire.* New York: W.W. Norton & Company, 1968.

Ferrante, Louis. *Unlocked: The Life and Crimes of a Mafia Insider.* New York: Harper Paperbacks, 2009.

The Five Books of Moses: Genesis, Exodus, Leviticus, Numbers, and Deuteronomy. The Schocken Bible. Translated by Everett Fox. Vol. 1 New York: Schocken Books, 1995.

Folsing, Albrecht. *Albert Einstein: A Biography.* Translated by Ewald Oser. New York: Viking, 1997.

Francis Bacon. Great Books of the Western World. Robert Maynard Hutchins, Editor in Chief. Vol. 30 Chicago: Encyclopaedia Britannica, Inc., 1952.

Frank, Philipp. *Einstein: His Life and Times.* Translated by George Rosen. Edited and Revised by Shuichi Kusaka. New York: Da Capo Press, [1989] 1947.

Freud, Sigmund. *An Autobiographical Study.* 4th Impression. The International Psycho-Analytical Library Series, no. 26. Edited by Ernest Jones. Authorized Translation by James Strachey. London: Hogarth Press, 1948.

---. *Beyond the Pleasure Principle.* Translated by James Strachey. Seattle, WA: Pacific Publishing Studio, 2010.

---. *Civilization and Its Discontents.* Newly Translated and Edited by James Strachey. College Edition. New York: W.W. Norton & Company, 1961.

---. *Collected Papers.* Authorized Translation Under the Supervision of Joan Riviere. 5 Vols. New York: Basic Books, 1959.

---. *The Complete Letters of Sigmund Freud to Wilhelm Fliess, 1887-1904*. Edited and Translated by Jeffrey Moussaieff Masson. Cambridge, MA: Belknap Press, 1985.

---. *Freud: Dictionary of Psychoanalysis.* Edited by Nandor Fodor and Frank Gaynor. Greenwich, CT: Fawcett Publications, 1966.

---. *The Interpretation of Dreams.* 8th ed., rev. Translated from the German and Edited by James Strachey. New York: Avon Books, 1965.

---. *Moses and Monotheism.* Translated by Katherine Jones. New York: Vintage Books, 1967.

---. *On the History of the Psycho-Analytic Movement.* Revised and Edited by James Strachey. Translated by Joan Riviere. New York: W.W. Norton & Company, 1966.

---. *The Origins of Psycho-Analysis: Letters to Wilhelm Fliess, Drafts, and Notes*. Edited by Marie Bonaparte, Anna Freud, and Ernest Kris. Translated by Eric Mosbacher and James Strachey. New York: Basic Books, 1950.

---. *The Psychopathology of Everyday Life.* The Standard Edition. Translated and Edited by James Strachey. New York: W.W. Norton & Company, 1965.

---. *Sigmund Freud: His Life in Pictures and Words*. Edited by Ernst Freud, Lucie Freud, and Ilse Grubrich-Simitis. Translation by Christine Trollope. New York: Harcourt Brace Jovanovich, 1978.

Freud, Sigmund, and Karl Abraham. *The Complete Correspondence of Sigmund Freud and Karl Abraham: 1907-1925: Complete Edition.* Edited by Ernst Falzeder. Translated by Caroline Schwarzacher, with the Collaboration of Christine Trollope and Klara Majthenyi King. London: Karnac Books, 2002.

Freud, Sigmund, and Sándor Ferenczi. *The Correspondence of Sigmund Freud and Sándor Ferenczi: Volume 1, 1908-1914.* Edited by Ernst Falzeder, Eva Brabant, and Patrizia Giampieri-Deutsch. Translated by Peter T. Hoffer. Cambridge, MA: Belknap Press of Harvard University Press, 1993.

Freud, Sigmund, and Sándor Ferenczi. *The Correspondence of Sigmund Freud and Sándor Ferenczi: Volume 3, 1920-1933.* Edited by Ernst Falzeder and Eva Brabant, with the Collaboration of Patrizia Giampieri-Deutsch. Translated by Peter T. Hoffer. Cambridge, MA: Belknap Press of Harvard University Press, 2000.

Freud, Sigmund, and Ernest Jones. *The Complete Correspondence of Sigmund Freud and Ernest Jones, 1908-1933.* Edited by R. Andrew Paskauskas. Cambridge, MA: Belknap Press of Harvard University Press, 1993.

Fromm, Erich. *Greatness and Limitations of Freud's Thought.* New York: Harper & Row, Publishers, 1980.

---. *Sigmund Freud's Mission: An Analysis of His Personality and Influence.* New York: Harper & Brothers Publishers, 1959.

Galilei, Galileo. *Dialogue Concerning the Two Chief World Systems: Ptolemaic and Copernican.* 2nd rev. ed. Translated by Stillman Drake. Berkley: CA: University of California Press, 1967.

Galison, Peter. *Einstein's Clocks, Poincaré's Maps: Empires of Time.* New York: W.W. Norton & Company, 2003.

Gay, Peter. *Freud: A Life for Our Time.* New York: W.W. Norton & Company, 1988.

Gilbert, Martin. *The First World War: A Complete History.* New York: Henry Holt and Company, 1994.

Gleitman, Henry, Alan J. Fridlund, and Daniel Reisberg. *Basic Psychology.* 5th ed. New York: W.W. Norton & Company, 2000.

Goldstein, E. Bruce. *Sensation and Perception.* 8th ed. Belmont, CA: Wadsworth Cengage Learning, 2010.

Gorst, Martin. *Measuring Eternity: The Search for the Beginning of Time.* New York: Broadway Books, 2001.

Graves, Robert. *Good-Bye to All That: An Autobiography*, New Edition, Revised. New York: Anchor Books, 1998.

Greene, Brian. *The Fabric of the Cosmos: Space, Time, and the Texture of Reality.* New York: Alfred A. Knopf, 2004.

Hadfield, J.A. *Dreams and Nightmares.* Baltimore, MD: Penguin Books, 1964.

Hall, Calvin S. *A Primer of Freudian Psychology.* New York: World Publishing Company, 1954.

Hippocrates. *The Medical Works of Hippocrates.* Translated by John Chadwick and W.N. Mann. Oxford: Blackwell, 1950.

Hitler, Adolf. *Mein Kampf.* Translated by Ralph
Manheim. New York: Houghton Mifflin Company, 1971.

Hobson, J. Allan. *The Dreaming Brain: How the Brain
Creates Both the Sense and the Nonsense of Dreams.* New
York: Basic Books, 1988.

Hoffer, Eric. *The True Believer: Thoughts on the Nature
of Mass Movements.* New York: Perennial Classics, 2002.

Hoffmann, Banesh, with the collaboration of Helen
Dukas. *Albert Einstein: Creator and Rebel.* New York:
Viking Press, 1973.

Holmes, Richard. *The Age of Wonder: How the Romantic
Generation Discovered the Beauty and Terror of Science.*
New York: Vintage Books, 2008.

Hooper, Judith, and Dick Teresi. *The Three Pound
Universe.* New York: Macmillan, 1986.

Isaacson, Walter. *Einstein: His Life and Universe.* New
York: Simon & Schuster Paperbacks, 2007.

Jones, Ernest. *The Life and Work of Sigmund Freud.* 3
Vols. New York: Basic Books, 1957.

---. *Sigmund Freud: Four Centenary Addresses.* New
York: Basic Books, 1956.

Jouvet, Michel. *The Paradox of Sleep: The Story of
Dreaming.* Translated be Laurence Garey. Cambridge,
MA: MIT Press, 1999.

Kahneman, Daniel. *Thinking, Fast and Slow.* New York:
Farrar, Straus, and Giroux, 2011.

Keegan, John. *The First World War.* New York: Alfred A. Knopf, 1999.

Kuhn, Thomas S. *The Structure of Scientific Revolutions.* Third edition. Chicago: University of Chicago Press, 1996.

Laing, R.D. *The Divided Self.* New York: Pantheon Books, 1960.

Las Cases, Emmanuel-Auguste-Dieudonné. *Mémorial de Sainte Hélène: Journal of the Private Life and Conversations of the Emperor Napoleon at Saint Helena.* Vol. 4 London: Henry Colburn & Co., 1823.

Lawrence, D.H. *The Letters of D.H. Lawrence. Volume 1: 1901-13.* Edited by James T. Boulton. The Cambridge Edition. Cambridge, England: Cambridge University Press, 2002.

Le Bon, Gustave. *The Crowd: A Study of the Popular Mind.* An unabridged republication of the second English-language edition of the work originally published in 1895 in France as *La Psychologie des Foules.* Translated by T. Fisher Unwin. Mineola, NY: Dover, 2002.

Le Doux, J. *The Emotional Brain.* New York: Simon &Schuster, 1996.

Libet, Benjamin. *Mind Time: The Temporal Factor in Consciousness, Perspectives in Cognitive Neuroscience.* Cambridge, MA: Harvard University Press, 2004.

Libet, Benjamin, Anthony Freeman, and J. K. B. Sutherland, Editors, *The Volitional Brain: Towards a Neuroscience of Free Will.* Exeter, UK: Imprint Academic, 1999.

Machiavelli Hobbes. Great Books of the Western World.
Editor in Chief Robert Maynard Hutchins. Vol. 23
Chicago: Encyclopaedia Britannica, 1952.

Menninger, Karl. *The Human Mind.* New York: Literary
Guild of America, 1930.

---. *Theory of Psychoanalytic Technique.* New York:
Basic Books, 1958.

Miles, Barry. *Paul McCartney: Many Years From Now.*
New York: Henry Holt and Company, 1997.

Miller, Arthur J., *Albert Einstein's Special Theory of
Relativity: Emergence (1905) and Early Interpretation,
(1905-1911).* New York: Springer Verlag, 1998.

Mind and Brain. Journey Through the Mind and Body
Series. By the Editors of Time-Life Books. Alexandria,
VA: Time-Life Books, 1993.

Minkowski, Hermann. *Space and Time: Minkowski's
Papers on Relativity.* Edited by Vesselin Petkov.
Translated by Fritz Lewertoff and Vesselin Petkov.
Montreal, Quebec, Canada: Minkowski Institute Press,
2012.

Minsky, Marvin. *The Society of Mind.* New York: Simon
& Schuster, 1986.

Morton, Alexandra. *Listening to Whales: What the Orcas
Have Taught Us.* New York: Ballantine Books,
2002/2004.

Mosley, Michael, and John Lynch. *The Story of Science:
Power, Proof, and Passion.* London: Octopus Publishing
Group, 2010.

The New Encyclopaedia Britannica, 15th ed. Article Editors David Foulkes, Wilse B. Webb, and Rosalind D. Cartwright. Vol. 27 Chicago: Encyclopaedia Britannica, Inc., 1991.

Nicolelis, Miguel. *Beyond Boundaries: The New Neuroscience of Connecting Brains With Machines—And How It Will Change Our Lives.* New York: Times Books/Henry Holt and Company, 2011.

The Origins of Science. Volume 1, Moments of Discovery. Edited by George Schwartz and Philip W. Bishop. New York: Basic Books, 1958.

The Oxford Companion to the Mind. Edited by Richard L. Gregory. New York: Oxford University Press, 1987.

Pais, Abraham. *Subtle is the Lord: The Science and the Life of Albert Einstein.* New York: Oxford University Press, 2005.

Panek, Richard. *The Invisible Century: Einstein, Freud, and the Search for Hidden Universes.* New York: Viking, 2004.

Penfield, Wilder. *The Mystery of the Mind: A Critical Study of Consciousness and the Human Brain.* Princeton, NJ: Princeton University Press, 1975.

Philo. *The Works of Philo: Complete and Unabridged in One Volume.* New updated edition. Translated by C.D. Yonge. Peabody, MA: Hendrickson Publishers, 1993.

Question of Time: The Ultimate Paradox. Editors of Scientific American, 2012.

Radin, Dean. *Entangled Minds: Extrasensory Experiences in a Quantum Reality.* New York: Paraview Pocket Books, 2006.

Restak, Richard M. *The Brain Has a Mind of Its Own: Insights From a Practicing Neurologist.* New York: Harmony Books, 1991.

---. *The Brain: The Last Frontier.* New York: Warner Books, 1979.

---. *The Mind.* New York: Bantam Books, 1988.

Rich, Norman. *Hitler's War Aims: Ideology, the Nazi State, and the Course of Expansion.* New York: W.W. Norton & Co., 1973.

Robb, Graham. *Victor Hugo: A Biography.* New York: W.W. Norton & Company, 1997.

Rock, Andrea. *The Mind at Night: The New Science of How and Why We Dream.* New York: Basic Books, 2004.

Rosenblum, Bruce, and Fred Kuttner. *Quantum Enigma: Physics Encounters Consciousness.* New York: Oxford University Press, 2006.

Rosenthal-Schneider, Ilse. *Relativity and Scientific Truth: Discussions with Einstein, Von Laue, and Planck.* Detroit, IL: Wayne State University Press, 1980.

Schopenhauer, Arthur. *Essay on Freedom of the Will.* Dover Philosophical Classics Series. Translated by Konstantin Kolenda. Mineola, NY: Dover, 2005.

---. *On the Fourfold Root of the Principle of Sufficient Reason*. Translated by Mme. Karl Hillebrand. New York: Cosimo, Inc., 2007.

Schrödinger, Erwin. *Mind and Matter: The Tarner Lectures Delivered at Trinity College*. Cambridge: Cambridge University Press, 1958.

---. *What is Life?: And Mind and Matter*. London: Cambridge University Press, 1969.

Schwartz, Jeffrey M., and Sharon Begley. *The Mind and the Brain: Neuroplasticity and the Power of Mental Force*. New York: ReganBooks, 2002.

Sechrist, Elsie. *Dreams: Your Magic Mirror. With Interpretations of Edgar Cayce*. New York: Dell Publishing Co., 1968.

Seelig, Carl. *Albert Einstein: A Documentary Biography*. Translated by Mervyn Savill. London: Staples Press, 1956.

Shelley, Mary. *Frankenstein, or The Modern Prometheus*. Boston: Sever, Francis & Co., 1869.

Sherrington, Sir Charles. *The Integrative Action of the Nervous System*. Second Edition. New Haven, CT: Yale University Press, 1947.

Shirer, William L. *The Rise and Fall of the Third Reich: A History of Nazi Germany*. New York: MJF Books, 1990.

Stevenson, Robert Louis. *Across the Plains and Other Memories and Essays*. New York: Charles Scribner's Sons, 1912.

Strathern, Paul. *Mendeleyev's Dream: The Quest for the Elements*. New York: Thomas Dunne Books, 2001.

Talamonte, Leo. *The Forbidden Universe: Mysteries of the Psychic World*. Translated by Paul Stevenson. New York: Stein and Day, 1975.

Talmey, Max. *The Relativity Theory Simplified and the Formative Years of Its Inventor*. New York: Falcon Press, 1932.

Taylor, A.J.P. *Bismarck: The Man and the Statesman*. New York: Vintage Books, 1967.

Trefil, James. *101 Things You Don't Know About Science and No One Else Does Either*. Boston: Houghton Mifflin Company, 1996.

Ullman, Montague, Stanley Krippner, with Alan Vaughan. *Dream Telepathy*. New York: Macmillan Publishing Co., 1973.

Vallentin, Antonina. *The Drama of Albert Einstein*. Translated by Moura Budberg. New York: Doubleday, 1954.

Van de Castle, Robert L. *Our Dreaming Mind: A Sweeping Exploration of the Role That Dreams Have Played in Politics, Art, Religion, and Psychology, From Ancient Civilizations to the Present Day*. New York: Ballantine Books, 1994.

Voltaire, François Marie Arouet de. *The Portable Voltaire*. Edited by Ben Ray Redman. New York: Penguin Books, 1977.

Wagner, Richard, and Mathilde Wesendonck. *Richard Wagner to Mathilde Wesendonck.* Translated by William Ashton Ellis. New York: Charles Scribner's Sons, 1905.

Watson, James D. *The Double Helix: A Personal Account of the Discovery of the Structure of DNA.* New York: Atheneum, 1968.

Watt, Richard M. *The Kings Depart: The Tragedy of Germany: Versailles and the German Revolution.* New York: Simon & Schuster, 1968.

Weber, E. H. *E. H. Weber On the Tactile Senses.* Second Edition. Edited and Translated by Helen E. Ross and David J. Murray. Hove, UK: Erlbaum, Taylor & Francis, 1996.

Wehr, Gerhard. *Jung: A Biography.* Translated by David M. Weeks. Boston: Shambhala, 2001.

Wells, H.G. *The Time Machine, and The Invisible Man.* New York: Barnes and Noble Classics, 2003.

Wheeler, John Archibald, and Wojciech Hubert Zurek, Editors. *Quantum Theory and Measurement.* Princeton, NJ: Princeton University Press, 1983.

Yourgrau, Palle. *A World Without Time: The Forgotten Legacy of Gödel and Einstein.* New York: Basic Books, 2005.

Zimbardo, Philip, and John Boyd. *The Time Paradox: The New Psychology of Time That Will Change Your Life.* Waterville, ME: Thorndike Press, 2008.

Zukav, Gary. *The Dancing Wu Lu Masters: An Overview of the New Physics.* New York: Perennial Classics, 2001.

ARTICLES

Adolphs, Ralph, Daniel Tranel, and Antonio R. Damasio. "The Human Amygdala in Social Judgment." *Nature* 393 (1998): 470-474.

Bernstein, Jeremy. "A Critic at Large: Besso." *The New Yorker*, February 27, 1989.

Bierman, Dick J., and H. Steven Scholte. "Anomalous Anticipatory Brain Activation Preceding Exposure of Emotional and Neutral Pictures." *Journal of Parapsychology* 66, Issue 3 (2002).

Bierman, Dick J., and H. Steven Scholte. "Anomalous Anticipatory Brain Activation Preceding Exposure of Emotional and Neutral Pictures," Proceedings from the Parapsychological Association 45th Annual Convention, Paris, France, August 5-8, 2002.

Critchley, Hugo D., et al. "Neural Activity Relating to Generation and Representation of Galvanic Skin Conductance Responses: A Functional Magnetic Resonance Imaging Study." *The Journal of Neuroscience* 20, no. 8 (2000): 3033-3040.

Critchley, Hugo D., Christopher J. Mathias, and Raymond J. Dolan. "Fear Conditioning in Humans: The Influence of Awareness and Autonomic Arousal on Functional Neuroanatomy." *Neuron* 33, no. 4 (2002): 653-663.

Dement, William, and Nathaniel Kleitman. "The Relation of Eye Movement During Sleep to Dream Activity: An Objective Method for the Study of Dreaming." *Journal of Experimental Psychology* 53, no. 5 (1957): 339-346.

Diamond, Marian C., et al., "On the Brain of a Scientist: Albert Einstein." *Experimental Neurology* 88 (1985): 198-204.

Dimberg, Ulf, Monika Thunberg, and Kurt Elmehed. "Research Report: Unconscious Facial Reactions to Emotional Facial Expressions." *Psychological Science* 11, no. 1 (January 2000): 86-89.

"Dr. Hans Albert Einstein Dies; Physicist Was River Authority; Overcame Fame Problem." *New York Times*, July 27, 1973.

Feinstein, Justin S., et al. "The Human Amygdala and the Induction and Experience of Fear." *Current Biology*, 21, no. 1 (2011): 34-38.

Furmark, Tomas, et al. "The Amygdala and Individual Differences in Human Fear Conditioning." *NeuroReport* 8 (1997): 3957-3960.

Glascher, Jan, and Ralph Adolphs. "Processing of the Arousal of Subliminal and Supraliminal Emotional Stimuli by the Human Amygdala." *The Journal of Neuroscience* 23, no. 32 (November 12, 2003): 10274-10282.

Gross, Charles G. "Aristotle on the Brain," *The Neuroscientist* 1, no. 4 (1995): 245-250.

Hamann, Stephan B., et al. "Ecstasy and Agony: Activation of the Human Amygdala." *Psychological Science* 13, no. 2 (2002): 135-141.

"Is This Really Proof That Man Can See Into the Future?" *Daily Mail*, London. May 4, 2007. http://www.dailymail.co.uk/sciencetech/article-452833/Is-REALLY-proof-man-future.html

Kedrov, B.M. "On the Question of the Psychology of Scientific Creativity (On the Occasion of the Discovery by D.I. Mendeleev of the Periodic Law)." *Soviet Review* 8, no. 2 (1967): 26-45. This is an English translation of an earlier article which originally appeared in *Voprosy Psikhologgi* 3, no. 6 (1957): 91-113.

Libet, Benjamin. "Unconscious Cerebral Initiative and the Role of Conscious Will in Voluntary Action." *Behavioral and Brain Sciences* 8, Issue 4 (1985): 529-566.

Libet, Benjamin, et al. "Time of Unconscious Intention to Act in Relation to Onset of Cerebral Activity (Readiness-Potential): The Unconscious Initiation of a Freely Voluntary Act." *Brain* 106 (1983): 623-642.

Miller, William. "Death of a Genius: His Fourth Dimension, Time, Overtakes Einstein. Old Man's Advice to Youth: 'Never Lose a Holy Curiosity.'" *Life* 38, no. 18 (May 2, 1955): pp. 61-64.

Morris, J., A. Ohman, and R.J. Dolan. "Conscious and Unconscious Emotional Learning in the Human Amygdala." *Nature* 393, no. 6684(1998): 467–470.

Mossbridge, Julia, Patrizio Tressoldi, and Jessica Utts. "Predictive Physiological Anticipation Preceding Seemingly Unpredictable Stimuli." *Frontiers in Psychology* 3, Article 390 (2012): 1-18.

Niemann, Dr. Hildegard, and Dr. Christian Maschke. "WHO LARES: Final Report Noise Effects and Morbidity." Copenhagen, Denmark: WHO Regional Office for Europe, (2004).

Portas, Chiara M., et al. "Auditory Processing Across the Sleep-Wake Cycle: Simultaneous EEG and fMRI Monitoring in Humans." *Neuron* 28, no. 3 (2000): 991-999.

Radin, Dean I. "Electrodermal Presentiments of Future Emotions." *Journal of Scientific Exploration* 18, no. 2. (2004): 253-273.

Radin, Dean, and Ana Borges. "Intuition Through Time: What Does the Seer See?" *Explore* 5, no. 4 (2009): 200-211.

Sander, David, Jordan Grafman, and Tiziana Zalla. "The Human Amygdala: An Evolved System for Relevance Detection." *Reviews in the Neurosciences* 14, no. 4, (2003): 303-316.

Spottiswoode, S. James P., and Edwin C. May. "Skin Conductance Prestimulus Response: Analyses, Artifacts, and a Pilot Study." *Journal of Scientific Exploration* 17, no. 4 (2003): 617-641.

Viereck, George Sylvester. "What Life Means to Einstein: An Interview by George Sylvester Viereck." *The Saturday Evening Post*, October 26, 1929, pp. 17, 110-114, 117.

Whalen, Paul J., et al. "Masked Presentations of Emotional Facial Expressions Modulate Amygdala Activity Without Explicit Knowledge." *Journal of Neuroscience*, 18, no. 1 (1998): 411–418.

Winston, J.S., et al. "Automatic and Intentional Brain
Responses During Evaluation of Trustworthiness of
Faces." *Nature Neuroscience* 5, no. 3 (2002): 277-283.

Witelson, Sandra F., Debra L. Kigar, and Thomas Harvey.
"The Exceptional Brain of Albert Einstein." *Lancet* 353,
no. 9170 (1999): 2149-53.

ELECTRONIC SOURCES

Cromie, William J. "Research Links Sleep, Dreams, and
Learning." *The Harvard University Gazette*, February 8,
1996.
http://www.news.harvard.edu/gazette/1996/02.08/Researc
hLinksSl.html

Federal Express Commercial with "Motormouth" John
Moschitta. Accessed September 27, 2013.
http://www.youtube.com/watch?v=NeK5ZjtpO-M

NPR *Science Friday* Radio Interview with Kary Mullis,
May 21, 1999.
http://www.sciencefriday.com/segment/05/21/1999/kary-
mullis.html

About the Author

Louis Ferrante is a television host, motivational speaker, and international bestselling author. His books have been translated into fifteen languages. He has appeared as a commentator on television networks such as MSNBC, Fox News, History Channel, CBC, and the BBC.

Following his hugely successful Discovery Channel series, Lou was nominated for a Grierson Award, one of the world's most prestigious documentary awards.

For his contribution to literacy in the United Kingdom, Lou was given the Celebrity Reading Hero Award, presented to him at Number 10 Downing Street.

Lou's previous books include his memoir, *Unlocked: The Life and Crimes of a Mafia Insider*, and his international bestseller, *Mob Rules: What the Mafia Can Teach the Legitimate Businessman.*

Help start the conversation at:

TheThreePoundCrystalBall.com

LouisFerrante.com

@LouFerrante

Made in the USA
Lexington, KY
05 June 2015